MYTHS AND LEGENDS

Edited by
Anne Marie Mueser

D1020458

CURRICULUM CONSULTANT

John J. Kegan
Principal, Netherwood School
Hyde Park, New York
N.Y. State English/Language Arts
Turnkey Trainer for Northeastern
and Metropolitan New York

STAFF

Publisher: Eleanor Angeles
Editorial Director: Edward C. Haggerty
Series Editor: Marjorie Burns
Editor: Anne Marie Mueser, Ed.D.
Production: Harry Chester Associates
Cover Design: Marijka Kostiw

COVER: The sign of the Flying Red Horse was photographed on Route 60B near Mountain Grove, Missouri. It was at a Mobil gasoline station.
Photograph © John Margolies/ESTO.

Design of Scholastic Literature Anthologies based on concept by Joe Borzetta.

ISBN 0-590-35434-5

ACKNOWLEDGMENTS

Grateful acknowledgment is made to the following authors and publishers for the use of copyrighted materials. Every effort has been made to obtain permission to use previously published material. Any errors or omissions are unintentional.

Farrar Straus and Gireaux for an excerpt from MEN AND GODS by Rex Warner, published 1953.

David Higham Associates, Ltd., for "Pegasus" by Eleanor Farjeon from THE CHILDREN'S BELLS. Copyright © by Eleanor Farjeon.

Random House for "The Myth of Sisyphus" from THE MYTH OF SISYPHUS AND OTHER ESSAYS by Albert Camus, translated by Justin O'Brien. Copyright © 1953 by Alfred A. Knopf, Inc. "King Arthur's Place in the World" from KING ARTHUR AND HIS KNIGHTS by Mabel Louise Anderson. Copyright ©1953 by Random House.

Scholastic Inc. for "Echo and Narcissus" from THE GREEK GODS by Bernard and Dorothy Evslin and Ned Hoopes. Copyright © 1966 by Scholastic Inc. for "Phaethon: Son of the Sun," retold by Aille X. West, from HOW TO READ LITERATURE, Level One. Copyright © 1986 by Annie Mueser Associates, Ltd.

Viking Penguin, a division of Penguin Books USA, Inc. for "Orpheus" from THE TIGER'S BONES AND OTHER PLAYS FOR CHILDREN by Ted Hughes. Copyright © 1974 by Ted Hughes.

Houghton Mifflin Company for an excerpt from WORDS FROM THE MYTHS by Isaac Asimov. Copyright © 1961, 1969 by Isaac Asimov. Reprinted by permission of Houghton Mifflin Company.

Little, Brown and Company, for an excerpt and illustrations from MYTHOLOGY by Edith Hamilton, illustrated by Steele Savage. Copyright © 1942 by Edith Hamilton: Copyright © renewed 1969 by Dorian Fielding Reid and Doris Fielding Reid. By permission of Little, Brown and Company.

ILLUSTRATIONS

The illustrations on pages 18, 36, 60, 78, 104, 132, 152, 176 are by Steele Savage, from MYTHOLOGY by Edith Hamilton.

CONTENTS

I. In the Beginning...
From Chaos to
Cosmos

The ancient Greeks believed that in the beginning there was *Chaos*. They imagined that the universe was made up of a great confused mass of raw material — without form or shape, but with the potential for all that was to come. The Greeks called this mass of raw material *Chaos*. (In Greek, the word "chaos" means an open gulf. The vast reaches of outer space, before the stars and planets were formed, might well have been imagined by the ancient peoples to be an open gulf, with nothing visible or formed.)

Out of the confusion of *Chaos* came things with form and shape. The Greeks called the result *Cosmos*. The word "cosmos," in Greek, means order or good arrangement. *Cosmos*, therefore, was a very suitable word for the order which emerged out of *Chaos*. Today, the universe is often referred to as the "cosmos."

The ancient Greeks believed that the first beings to come out of *Chaos* were *Gaia (Gaea)* and *Ouranos (Uranus),* or earth and sky. They thought of the two as man and wife, who had children of enormous size and strength. These children probably symbolized the enormous and destructive forces of nature.

Among the gigantic offspring of Gaia and Ouranos were a group of creatures, both male and female, who were known as Titans and Titanesses. One of them, Cronus, drove their father away and became chief. Cronus and his wife Rhea, an early version of an earth goddess, had a number of children. Cronus kept his children under control in a most unusual way until Zeus, with the help of Rhea, was able to overthrow the rule of Cronus.

One of the most important and best known of the Titans was Atlas, who battled the younger gods in an effort to maintain Titan rule. The Greeks believed that when the Titans were defeated, Atlas was forced to support the heavens on his shoulders as eternal punishment for his role as a Titan leader.

From the Myths

THE FAMILY OF CRONUS

● Cronus (Saturn) and Rhea (Ops) were Titans, the children of earth and sky. Cronus, who believed that one of his own offspring would eventually dethrone him, took extraordinary means to ensure that such a happening would never occur.

FOR AGES AND AGES, CRONUS AND RHEA RULED heaven and earth. They had six children, three of them sons and three of them daughters. Cronus, however, had been forewarned that one of his own children would dethrone him. He knew that such a thing could happen, because he had murdered his own father to assume his position. In order to avoid meeting the same fate he had inflicted on his father, Cronus swallowed each one of his infant children as soon as he or she was born.

Rhea, mother of the consumed children, became quite tired of losing her offspring in this bizarre manner. After losing five children, she decided that enough was enough. When her sixth child was born, she wrapped a stone in swaddling clothes as she would have wrapped an infant. She handed the bundle to Cronus, who promptly swallowed it. The real baby, whom she named Zeus, was sent to the isle of Crete where he was looked after by nymphs[1] and raised on goat's milk.

In due time, Zeus reached maturity. He returned to the region of his birth and, with the help of his grandmother, forced his father to disgorge[2] the five children who had been swallowed earlier. Because they were gods, they survived the ordeal nicely and emerged quite unscathed.[3] Now Zeus was joined by his sisters Hera, Hestia, and Demeter, and by his brothers Poseidon and Hades.

With the help of his brothers and sisters, Zeus was determined to overthrow Cronus and seek vengeance for the old god's treatment of them. Most of the Titans sided with Cronus. Zeus and his siblings, however, were aided by the Cyclopes and the Hecatonchires, all of whom had been confined by Cronus to Tartarus, the depths of the underworld. The Cyclopes, one-eyed monsters of whom there were three, represented the terrors of rolling thunder, of the lightning flash, and of the thunderbolt. There were also three Hecatonchires, who were monsters each with a hundred hands.

Without the Cyclopes and the Hecatonchires, Zeus and his followers would not have been able to defeat the Titans. The Titans were ultimately beaten by the blinding lightning and the all-consuming fires set off by the Cyclopes and the shattering earthquakes precipitated by the hundred-handed monsters who shook the very hills as they fought.

Following their defeat of the Titans, the victorious gods led by Zeus ruled from Mount Olympus. Their reign was not without conflict, however. Gaea, the grandmother of Zeus who had aided her grandson in the war against Cronus, developed pangs of conscience for having done so. To help avenge the suffering the Titans had endured at the hands of the Olympians, Gaea gave birth to another son—a monster

9

called Typhon—whose purpose in life was to battle Zeus. Typhon's neck sprouted a hundred dragonheads, his eyes spouted fire, and his tongues created the most dreadful noises—hisses, roars, bellows, barks, and screams. Using his thunderbolt, Zeus managed to send Typhon to Tartarus where, it was said, the monster still managed to send frightening fire and great noises to earth through the craters of active volcanoes.

Long after banishing Typhon to Tartarus, the gods had to deal with the Giants, a race of creatures somewhat more like men than monsters. The Giants clothed themselves in animal skins, and used rocks and trees as weapons. They had the bodies of snakes for lower limbs, and their appearance was ghastly and frightening. In due course, however, the Giants were banished forever to Tartarus.

[1] **nymphs:** maidens who were lesser gods in mythology (usually associated with some aspect of nature)
[2] **disgorge:** throw up (from the stomach or mouth); yield
[3] **unscathed:** not harmed

A CLOSER LOOK

1. Why did Cronus fear his own children? How did he deal with his fear? Were his fears justified? Do you think what he did was appropriate? Why, or why not?

2. Would you describe Rhea as a good mother? Why, or why not?

3. Why do you think Gaea at first was willing to help Zeus defeat Cronus? Why and how did she show remorse for what she had done?

From the Myths

ATLAS

• Atlas was a Titan who fought hard and well against Zeus and the other Olympians who were trying to overthrow Cronus. When the Titans lost, Atlas was punished severely. Even today, Atlas is thought of as having the weight of the world on his shoulders.

ATLAS WAS A POWERFUL TITAN WHO FOUGHT SO fiercely and so bravely in the war against the gods that he was singled out for special punishment when the Titans were defeated and exiled to Tartarus. Atlas was condemned to stand on the edge of the world and bear the heavens on his shoulders.

Centuries passed and still Atlas stood unrelieved of his burden. At one time he had been married to the Titaness Pleione. Among his offspring were the Pleiades and the Hyades, two groups of seven sisters each of which now graces the heavens as constellations[1] of stars. Atlas was also the father of Calypso, on whose island Odysseus took refuge for seven years during his journey home after the Trojan War.

In addition to the Pleiades, and the Hyades, Atlas had another group of daughters known as the Hesperides. These three lovely maidens, the apple nymphs, went with their father into exile. They guarded Hera's golden apple tree that grew in Atlas's shadow.

The task to which Atlas was sentenced for eternity was a painful and tedious one which involved great physical exertion and suffering as well as mental anguish. According to one version of the myth, Atlas was relieved of his suffering by Perseus, the hero who killed Medusa. (See page 106.) It was said that anyone who gazed upon the head of Medusa would be turned to stone. Perseus, in an effort to free Atlas from eternal suffering, held the head of Medusa where Atlas could view it. Atlas looked at the head of Medusa, and by so doing, the great Titan was turned to stone. Now, where it was believed that Atlas once stood holding the heavens up on his shoulders, there are only rocky mountain peaks reaching toward the sky.

As the ancient peoples learned more about the universe, facts began to stand in the way of literal interpretation of certain of the myths. For example, the early notion that Atlas stood supporting the sky was not consistent with the emerging science of astronomy. The Greeks came to understand that the sky and the heavenly bodies in it were extremely far away—too far away for Atlas to reach them. They also realized that the sky—with or without Atlas— was unlikely to fall. As time went on, therefore, the story changed somewhat and Atlas was portrayed as holding up the world, not the heavens, on his shoulders. That image persists today.

[1] **constellations:** groups of stars

A CLOSER LOOK

1. Why was Atlas sentenced to eternal punishment? Do you think the punishment was deserved? Why, or why not?

2. How did the Greeks' description of the punishment of Atlas change as they learned more about the universe?

From the Myths

PROMETHEUS AND PANDORA

● At least one version of the ancient myths credits Prometheus with the creation of humankind. Prometheus was also held to be responsible for giving humans the gift of fire. In return, mortals and Prometheus were punished by Zeus. Pandora was a part of that punishment.

P ROMETHEUS WAS A TITAN WITH THE GIFT OF prophecy.[1] Because he knew in advance that the Titans would be unsuccessful in their battle with the Olympians, Prometheus was clever enough to side with the winners. When the conflict was over, Prometheus and his brother Epimetheus were given the assignment of making humankind and providing people and all the other animals with the faculties they needed to survive.

Epimetheus gave the different animals the various gifts such as courage, strength, cleverness, or swiftness. Some creatures received wings; others received claws, and so on. Prometheus, however, took it upon himself to make a creature in the image of the gods. He made humans to walk upright with their eyes toward the heavens rather than toward the ground beneath their feet.

Epimetheus had been so extravagant[2] with his gifts to the other animals that there was nothing left to bestow on humankind that would be a special blessing. Prometheus, however came up with what he believed to be the perfect gift. He lighted his torch at the chariot of the sun and brought back fire. With fire in their possession, humans would be able to accomplish many things that would be otherwise denied.

Zeus was extremely vexed that Prometheus had given fire to mortals. Zeus had even been contemplating getting rid of all humans and creating a new race, but he had not yet managed to do so. The supreme god deprived the mortals of fire, but Prometheus stole the treasure once again from heaven and made it available for human use.

Zeus was so enraged that Prometheus had defied him that he inflicted a most cruel and unusual punishment. He ordered that Prometheus be chained to a rock on Mount Caucasus, where a vulture would come each day and prey upon the Titan's liver. Because the liver was not consumed, the punishment was continuous and potentially everlasting. Prometheus could have ended his ordeal by cooperating with Zeus and revealing a particular secret, but he chose not to do so.

The secret Zeus wanted Prometheus to tell involved the identity of the woman who would eventually bear him a son who would displace him and end the reign of the Olympians. Prometheus, having been both blessed and cursed with the power of prophecy, was thought to know the information Zeus sought. But Prometheus was willing to wait, because he also knew he would eventually be delivered from his torment by a hero whose father would be none other than the supreme god himself. (And the Titan's patience was rewarded, for in the thirteenth generation, as foretold, the great hero Hercules killed the vulture and freed Prometheus from the chains that bound him.)

In addition to the punishment inflicted directly on Prometheus, Zeus contrived a curse for mortals as well. Pandora, whose name means "the gift of all the gods," was created. Each god or goddess contributed something to Pandora, the first woman. Pandora was beautiful, strong, talented, and curious. Zeus presented her to Epimetheus who was delighted with the gift of so lovely a woman.

Pandora brought with her a lidded box which she had been instructed never to open. One day, however, she was completely overcome with curiosity. She simply could not resist opening the container. She opened the lid just enough to take a tiny peek, but even that was too much. As soon as the cover was lifted, out poured a panoply[3] of problems for humankind. Every manner of disease for the body and for the spirit, every possible evil that could befall mortals escaped from the box. Pandora instantly slammed down the cover, but she was too late to contain the evils. Only one thing remained, and that was hope.

One should not be too hasty to draw a conclusion that curiosity is a trait only to be found in women, of whom the Greeks believed Pandora to be the first example. There are some versions of the tale which claim that it was Epithemeus rather than Pandora who opened the box and released the ills which have troubled the world ever since.

[1] **prophecy:** foretelling or prediction of what is to come
[2] **extravagant:** wastefully generous
[3] **panoply:** a complete array of something

A CLOSER LOOK

1. In what ways did the gift of prophecy help Prometheus? How do you think things might have been different for him if he had been unable to see the future?

2. Why did Prometheus give fire to human beings? Why did this gift so enrage Zeus? What did Zeus do about it?

3. Who was Pandora? In what way was she part of the punishment Zeus devised for the mortals who had received the gift of fire?

● In this poem by the American poet Henry Wadsworth Longfellow the ordeal of Prometheus is seen as an inspiration to poets and to everyone.

Henry Wadsworth Longfellow

PROMETHEUS

O Prometheus, how undaunted
   On Olympus' shining bastions
His audacious foot he planted,
Myths are told, and songs are chanted,
   Full of promptings and suggestions.

Beautiful is the tradition
   Of that flight through heavenly portals,
The old classic superstition
Of the theft and the transmission
   Of the fire of the Immortals!

First the deed of noble daring,
   Born of heavenward aspiration,
Then the fire with mortals sharing,
Then the vulture,—the despairing
   Cry of pain on crags Caucasian.

All is but a symbol painted
   Of the Poet, Prophet, Seer;
Only those are crowned and sainted
Who with grief have been acquainted,
   Making nations nobler, freer.

In their feverish exultations,
   In their triumph and their yearning,
In their passionate pulsations,
In their words among the nations,
   The Promethean fire is burning.

Shall it, then, be unavailing,
   All this toil for human culture?
Through the cloud-rack, dark and trailing,
Must they see above them sailing
   O'er life's barren crags the vulture?

16

Such a fate as this was Dante's,
　By defeat and exile maddened;
Thus were Milton and Cervantes,
Nature's priests and Corybantes,
　By affliction touched and saddened.

But the glories so transcendent
　That around their memories cluster,
And, on all their steps attendant,
Make their darkened lives resplendent
　With such gleams of inward lustre!

All the melodies mysterious,
　Through the dreary darkness chanted;
Thoughts in attitudes imperious,
Voices soft, and deep, and serious,
　Words that whispered, songs that haunted!

All the soul in rapt suspension,
　All the quivering, palpitating
Chords of life in utmost tension,
With the fervor of invention,
　With the rapture of creating!

Ah, Prometheus! heaven-scaling!
　In such hours of exultation
Even the faintest heart, unquailing,
Might behold the vulture sailing
　Round the cloudy crags Caucasian!

Though to all there is not given
　Strength for such sublime endeavor,
Thus to scale the walls of heaven,
And to leaven with fiery leaven
　All the hearts of men forever;

Yet all bards, whose hearts unblighted
　Honor and believe the presage,
Hold aloft their torches lighted,
Gleaming through the realms benighted,
　As they onward bear the message!

II.   The Olympians

After many ages of supremacy in the universe, the Titans were overthrown and succeeded by the Olympians. There were twelve great Olympians, who were referred to by that name because Olympus was their home.

The abode and headquarters of the gods was believed to be on the summit of Mount Olympus, in the northeast part of Greece known as Thessaly. Olympus, Greece's highest peak, was believed by the ancient Greeks to be the center of the world. The gates to Olympus were clouds, managed by the goddesses named the Seasons. The celestials, or heavenly beings, passed through the cloud gates when necessary to conduct their business on earth, and upon their return to their Olympian home.

Of the twelve great Olympians, Zeus (Jupiter) was supreme among them, and the ruler of the heavens and sky. His brother Poseidon (Neptune) ruled the sea, while Hades (Pluto) ruled the underworld. Hera (Juno) was the wife of Zeus and the patroness of marriage. Ares (Mars), the god of war, was the son of Zeus and Hera. Athena (Minerva), the goddess of wisdom, was the daughter of Zeus. Athena had no mother, but was said to have emerged full grown from the head of Zeus to become his favorite offspring.

Zeus's children—Phoebus Apollo (known by the same name to both the Greeks and Romans), Aphrodite (Venus), Hermes (Mercury) and Artemis (Diana) were also part of the Olympian divine family. Apollo, who played many roles, was known as god of light, truth and the law, and also as the sun-god. Aphrodite was the goddess of love and beauty. Hermes, who was clever and cunning, created a place for himself on Olympus, and became messenger to the gods. Artemis, lover of wild things and the supreme huntress, was also goddess of the moon.

Zeus's sister, Hestia (Vesta) was the goddess of the earth, symbol of the home. Hephaestus (Vulcan) was the son of Hera and perhaps of Zeus, although some believed Hera created him on her own to repay Zeus for his creation of Athena. Hephaestus, who was both ugly and lame, was god of fire and patron of handicrafts, and a popular figure among mortals as well as the gods.

From the Myths

THE TWELVE OLYMPIANS

● There were twelve great gods of Olympus, each with a special realm and area of interest. Although the twelve had a number of similarities, they had many differences as well. As you read about each god or goddess, think about which traits could only have been those of a deity, and which were very human as well.

ZEUS (JUPITER)

ZEUS (JUPITER) BECAME THE SUPREME RULER OF THE Gods, the god of the sky and heavens, when he and his brothers drew lots. Poseidon became god of the sea, and Hades was assigned to the underworld. To Zeus went the greatest power. He presided over the sky, the rain, and the clouds, and one of his strongest and most feared weapons was the thunderbolt.

Zeus was very conscious of what he believed to be his supreme powers not only over mortals, but over all the gods as well. In Homer's *Iliad*, Zeus told his family that he was the mightiest of them all. He challenged them to try to budge him, and claimed that their combined strength could not equal his own. "Fasten a rope of gold to heaven and lay hold, every god and goddess," Zeus told them. "You could not drag down Zeus. But if I wished to drag you down, then I would. The rope I would bind to a pinnacle[1] of Olympus and all would hang in the air, yes the very earth and the sea too."

Despite his supreme confidence and might, Zeus did not possess perfect power or perfect knowledge of all things. He even seemed, at times, almost more human than ordinary mortals. In some matters, especially pertaining to affairs of the heart, he was quite vulnerable.[2]

Zeus frequently fell in love, and he found it necessary to employ elaborate stratagems to conceal his various acts of unfaithfulness from his wife Hera.

Why would Zeus, the god with the most power and majesty, have such complications in his relationships? One explanation is that the Zeus of whom storytellers and poets told was really a composite of many gods. When worship of Zeus spread to a place where there was already a ruling deity, the qualities of the two gods became intertwined. Zeus not only assumed the position and some of the attributes of the previous ruler, but in some cases acquired that god's spouse as well.

The complex details of the life and relationships of Zeus did not seem to diminish the aura of majesty and grandeur which surrounded the supreme god. Zeus was the dispenser of justice to individuals and to governments. His bird was no less than the mighty eagle, and his tree was the great oak. The will of Zeus was made known at the oracle of Dodona, where those who inquired about the future were provided with answers. It was said that the oracle spoke through the rustling of the oak leaves in the wind. Priests interpreted the sounds and communicated their meaning to the waiting faithful.

HERA (JUNO)

Hera (Juno) was both the sister and wife of Zeus. She was a child of Cronus and Rhea, as was Zeus, but she was brought up by the Titans Ocean and Tethys. Hera was viewed as the protector of married women, and many of the stories about her tell how she punished women who became involved with Zeus. Hera directed her implacable[3] wrath at any woman with whom her husband dallied.[4] Even those who had yielded to Zeus because he gave them no choice were severely punished.

When Hera singled out someone to punish, she was cruel and un-yielding. Callisto, for example, was a young maiden who aroused the passion of Zeus and the jealous rage of Hera. To punish her and take away her beauty, Hera turned Callisto into a bear. Although Callisto had the looks and growl of a bear, she still had the disposition and feelings of a woman. One day, Callisto recognized an approaching hunter as her own son. She raised her paws to embrace him and he raised his spear in defense. Zeus finally came to the aid of his former lover by sending both Callisto and her son to the heavens where they still can be seen as the constellations Big Bear and Little Bear.

Hera was quickly provoked to jealousy, and not only by other women. She was capable of holding a grudge for a very long time. Without her intervention, for example, the Trojan War might have been settled honorably in a way that destroyed neither side. But Hera was still angry at Aphrodite, the fairest goddess of them all, and she would not stop meddling in the war until Troy lay in ruins.

Hera's favorite city was Argos, and her sacred animals were the cow and the peacock. Despite her generally jealous nature and irritable disposition, Hera was venerated[5] in every home. It was to Hera that married women turned in time of need. Hera's daughter Ilithyia helped women in childbirth.

POSEIDON (NEPTUNE)

When the gods finally overcame the Titans, and Zeus became the supreme ruler of gods and men, Poseidon was given the responsibility of the seas and all the other waters of the earth. Of the twelve Olympians, Poseidon was second only to Zeus. Although he could often be found on Mount Olympus, Poseidon also had a magnificent palace in the depths of the ocean where he lived with his wife Amphitrite. From this palace in the deep he ruled his vast realm.

From time to time Poseidon could be seen, it was said, on the surface of the sea with his trident, a three pronged spear. Such occasions were likely to coincide with high winds, waves, and raging storms. As ruler of the sea, Poseidon was the one charged with bringing the waters under control. As he drove his golden chariot over the waters, the waters became calm.

Poseidon had a son named Triton, whose job it was to ensure that his father's commands were communicated to the waters everywhere. Triton is usually depicted with a great trumpet made of a shell with which he was believed to transmit order to the farthest reaches of the seas.

In addition to being Lord of the Sea, Poseidon was greatly honored for having granted the first horse to mortals. He was thought to preside over the world of horses and horsemanship as well as the many waters of the earth.

HADES (PLUTO)

Hades was also known as Pluto, the god of wealth, who presided over the precious metals of the earth. He was sometimes called Dis, the Latin word for rich. When the gods divided up the power after the Titans were defeated, Hades drew the Underworld, a place which he rarely left. He had a cap which made anyone who wore it invisible, and this enabled him to visit the upper world unnoticed if he so desired.

The wife of Hades was Persephone (Proserpine), who became Queen of the Underworld when Hades abducted her from her earthly home. (You'll find her story in Myths of the Underworld, beginning on page 61).

ARES (MARS)

Ares (Mars), the son of Zeus and Hera, was the god of war. He was not popular among the Greek people, and there were no cities in which any special places of worship were set up to honor him. Ares was disliked by gods and goddesses including his parents, who were said to detest him and his bloodthirsty ways.

The great Greek poet Homer described Ares as the scourge[6] of mortals, the piercer of shields, and one whose hands were bloodstained. Zeus once said to his son Ares, "Most hateful to me art thou of all the gods that dwell in Olympus; thou ever lovest strife and war and battles." It was believed that Ares enjoyed the carnage[7] of the battlefield, and this belief caused considerable disgust among his fellow deities and among mortals.

One goddess of Olympus, however, had a somewhat different opinion of Ares. That goddess was Aphrodite, the goddess of love and beauty, who found Ares so attractive that she became romantically involved with him for a time. The warrior Ares sometimes found peace and repose in the arms of Aphrodite. Most of the time, however, he was likely to be in the thick of the most devastating battles.

Mars, the Roman counterpart of Ares, was more popular among the Roman people than Ares was among the Greeks. This in part can be explained by the fact that the Romans were a warlike people whose goals included the relentless expansion of their empire. The bloody accomplishments of Mars served as inspiration rather than a cause for disgust. Unlike the Greeks, who preferred to ignore the god of war, the Romans built many temples for Mars and honored him with numerous celebrations throughout the year.

Another reason for the Roman devotion to the god of war may be found in the story of Romulus and Remus, who were said to be the offspring of Mars, and who founded the city of Rome.

The emblems of the god of war were the spear and the burning torch. The animals chosen by him as his special favorites were vultures[8] and dogs.

ATHENA (MINERVA)

Athena, the daughter of Zeus, had no mother, and one of the strangest of her stories is the tale of her birth. For some time, Zeus had been experiencing a severe and intense pain in his head. Suddenly his skull opened wide, and from it Athena sprang fully grown. It was no wonder that Zeus' headache had been painful. Athena emerged wearing the full armor of a warrior. Her head was helmeted, and she carried a spear which she brandished in a warlike manner.

In her early days, Athena was known as the Goddess of the Battle, and she was thought of as ruthless. Later, however, her warlike qualities were only employed when needed to defend the governmental body or the home from outside enemies. Athena was best known as the Goddess of the City of Athens and its people. She was considered a protector of civilized life, and a goddess of handicrafts and agriculture. As time went on, she became known as the goddess of wisdom and reason.

Athena was an elegantly beautiful and statuesque goddess with grey eyes and golden hair. Through her efforts to promote arts and letters, the ancient civilization flourished. She was held in extremely high esteem by the Greeks, who placed a high value on education and the arts. A magnificent temple called the Parthenon was erected on a hilltop in Athens, the special city of the goddess.

Athena's special gift to Greece was the olive tree, and it was through that gift that the goddess became the patroness of the city of Athens. There had been conflict between Athena and Poseidon over which one should rule Attica, the part of ancient Greece surrounding what was to become the city of Athens. It was agreed that the conflict would be resolved by granting the area to the one whose gift would be the most use to the local people. The other gods were to judge. Poseidon and Athena ascended a high hill called the Acropolis, and each bestowed a gift.

In one version of the tale, the god of the sea struck a boulder with his trident, causing a spring of fresh water to flow. In another version, Poseidon's gift was not fresh water but a horse. In both stories, however, Athena caused an olive tree to grow, and her gift was deemed most useful. She became, therefore, the ruler of the region.

Athena, perhaps because of the peculiar circumstances surrounding her birth, was the special favorite of her father. Zeus honored her above all other deities. He permitted her to wear his awful aegis, a shield emblazoned with the head of Medusa. He sometimes trusted her to carry his most feared weapon, the thunderbolt. Athena's special creature was the owl, and even today this bird is thought of as a symbol of wisdom.

ARTEMIS (DIANA)

Artemis was the daughter of Zeus and Leto, and the twin sister of Apollo. She loved wild things, and was considered the chief huntsman of the gods, a rather unusual post for a woman in ancient times. She had a great love for hunting, and the exhilaration of the chase was one of her most desired diversions. Mortals often told of hearing far off in the distance the baying of the hounds and the delighted cries of the nymphs as Artemis and her hunting parties pursued the wild boar and the stag.

Artemis, an unmarried goddess pledged to remain a maiden, took special care of young girls and often rescued them from difficulty. In return for the many kindnesses shown by the goddess, a young woman about to marry would bring her dolls to an altar of Artemis as an offering of gratitude.

Although Artemis was known for her kindness to the young, she could also be extremely cruel if it suited her to be so. The story of a young hunter named Actaeon is one example of her less noble side. One day Actaeon was hunting in the forest and quite by accident happened to catch a glimpse of the goddess bathing in a pool. Artemis was instantly enraged and totally unforgiving of the youth's unintended transgression. She changed Actaeon into a stag, and witnessed unmoved the young man's painful death as his own hounds tore him to bits because they were unable to recognize their master or comprehend his plea.

In addition to her role as huntress and protector of maidens, Artemis was also goddess of the moon. Moonbeams were her arrows, and it was said that she used them when needed to bestow a speedy and painless death on a woman. As the moon goddess, Artemis (also called Diana, or Cynthia) fell in love with the shepherd Endymion, and strayed briefly from her vow of maidenhood. (You will find the story of Diana and Endymion on page 95.)

Although Diana was the supreme huntress, and, as such, reveled in the thrill of the chase, there was a side of her which protected wild things. She loved horses and dogs, as well as the beasts of the forest. Her favorite animals were the boar, the goat, the bear, the dog, and especially the deer. Her sacred tree was the cypress.

HESTIA (VESTA)

Hestia, the goddess of the hearth, was the sister of Zeus, and a maiden goddess like Athena and Artemis. She presided over the home, the central symbol of which was the hearth. The hearth was the location of worship of this goddess as well as the place where the food necessary to sustain life was prepared. Before and after each meal, an offering was made to Hestia. To be accepted as a member of the family, a newborn baby was carried around the hearth and prayers were said to Hestia.

In addition to the hearth which was the center of every home, each city had a public hearth dedicated to the honor and glory of Hestia. The fire in the public hearth was kept as an eternal flame, and was not permitted to go out. When a new city was started, coals from the hearth of the city from which the settlers came were brought to light the flame in the new hearth.

In Rome, where the goddess was called by her Latin name, Vesta, the fire was tended by six maiden priestesses referred to as Vestals. Young women who volunteered to serve as Vestals had to pledge to remain virgins for thirty years, after which time they could marry if they chose to do so. Spirits known as the Lares and Penates were associated with Vesta in the home. The Lares (or Lar, in a home which had only one), were responsible for the general welfare, while the Penates specifically attended to the storehouse.

APHRODITE (VENUS)

Aphrodite, the goddess of love and beauty, was an extremely beguiling[10] and irresistible creature. Rare was the man or god who would not fall for her charms if given half a chance. In Homer's *Iliad*, Aphrodite was decribed as the daughter of Zeus and the nymph Dione. A far more interesting account which appeared in later poems, however, described how the goddess rose from the foam of the sea. She emerged near the island of Cythera, and then was wafted to Cyprus where she set foot on the shore. Both islands were forever sacred to her, and she was often referred to as Cytheria or the Cyprian.

Aphrodite symbolized the love between men and women, and the force that reproduces life in nature. She was worshipped everywhere throughout the ancient world, and her many altars could be found strewn with roses.

Eros (Cupid), the son of Venus, aided his mother in influencing affairs of the heart. He carried a bow and a quiver of arrows, some golden tipped and others tipped with lead. The golden ones caused both gods and mortals to fall in love, while the leaden ones had precisely the opposite effect. The image of Cupid that has come to us from the Romans is that of a mischievous boy depicted on valentine cards. The god the Greeks knew as Eros, however, was a dignified young man who took his obligations quite seriously.

Aphrodite, as the goddess of love, took part in many stories. Perhaps the best known historical event which she was said to have influenced was the Trojan War, which began with the apple awarded to her as the fairest goddess of them all. (You can read about the Trojan War and Aphrodite's role in it in Section VII, on page 134.) Aphrodite did not confine her efforts to famous people or notable historical events. She was believed to have heard and answered the cries of many unknown lovers who turned to her for help in moments of despair.

HEPHAESTUS (VULCAN)

Hephaestus, the God of Fire, was probably the son of Zeus and Hera, although some said Hera bore him on her own to punish Zeus for the way in which he brought forth Athena. In either case, however, there was agreement that Hephaestus was ugly in appearance, unlike the other immortals, who were exquisitely beautiful. Hephaestus was also lame. According to one story, Hephaestus was born crippled and Hera cast the deformed child out of heaven. Another story, however, blamed the god's lameness on Zeus. In that version, Hephaestus took the side of Hera in a quarrel she had with her husband. Zeus, who tolerated no such interference in his personal life, hurled Hera's son off Mount Olympus. The resulting injuries were said to be the reason Hephaestus was lame. If these events did occur, they apparently had no long term effects. Hephaestus had a firm place on Olympus where he performed much useful work and was greatly honored.

On Mount Olympus, Hephaestus was the workman of the deities. He made the weapons, armor, and numerous other items for the gods, and he constructed their houses and created the furnishings. It was said that he created handmaidens out of gold, and that they were able to help him with his work. The ancient Greeks and Romans sometimes explained the eruption of a volcano by suggesting that the forge of Hephaestus (or Vulcan) was beneath it.

Hephaestus was a kindly and peaceful god who was well liked by the other gods and by mortals. With Athena, he was patron of handicrafts, and he was the protector of smiths just as Athena was the protector of the weavers. In Homer's *Iliad*, the wife of Hephaestus was said to be one of the three Graces. In the *Odyssey* and other stories, however, Hephaestus is described as the husband of Aphrodite.

PHOEBUS APOLLO

Apollo, or Phoebus Apollo, who was known by the same name to both the Greeks and Romans, was the son of Zeus and Leto (Latona). He was born on the island of Delos. Artemis, the huntress and the Goddess of the Moon, was his twin.

Apollo was best known as the provider of light, the god of the sun. The Greeks understood how critical a role the sun played in their very survival, and they held Apollo in especially high esteem. They believed that he carried the sun across the sky from east to west each day in a chariot pulled by great horses. The Greeks associated healing powers with Apollo, and they gave the title of god of medicine to Apollo's son Aesculapius, who was such a skilled physician that, it was said, he could even bring the dead back to life.

Apollo was the ideal to which Greek men aspired. His physical perfection was an inspiration, and the Greeks encouraged their young men to emulate[11]Apollo's attributes of the body as well as of the mind. Track and field events, boxing, and wrestling were an integral part of the education of a Greek youth. Apollo was the patron of athletics, and Greek athletes prayed to him for success in athletic contests.

Apollo's appeal was not focused simply on the physical aspect of life. He was the giver of intellectual gifts, poetry, and song. Through the oracle at Delphi, Apollo was believed to communicate the truth to all who sought it. Many creatures were sacred to Apollo, and his special favorites were the dolphin and the crow. His tree was the laurel tree, and frequently a wreath of laurel was conferred in his honor to the winner of an athletic contest.

Although Apollo was considered to be an exquisite example of perfection of both physique and intellect, he was not always fortunate in affairs of the heart. He was known to take revenge on one who

displeased or rebuffed[12] him. For example, Cassandra, the daughter of King Priam of Troy to whom he had given the power of prophecy, displeased him in some way. He could not revoke the gift, but added to it that no one would believe Cassandra's predictions. When Cassandra forewarned the Trojans that they were about to be defeated in their ten-year war with Greece, everyone laughed at her. Shortly thereafter, however, Troy fell.

Apollo's treatment of Sibyl, a young woman who did not fancy him as he desired her, was similarly cruel. He offered her any gift within his power, and she asked that she might live as many years as there were grains of sand in a special place on the shore. Apollo granted her request, but because she would not marry him he did not confer immortality with it. As a result, Sibyl had to endure many centuries of life with the burdens of extreme old age.

Apollo's special fondness for the laurel tree began with yet another failed love affair. The nymph Daphne was so desperate to avoid Apollo's advances that she took a most extreme measure in her efforts to do so. (You will find out what this had to do with the laurel tree when you read the story of Apollo and Daphne on page 92.)

HERMES (MERCURY)

Hermes (Mercury) was the son of Zeus. His mother Maia was a daughter of Atlas. Hermes was perhaps the most clever of the gods. He was an extremely precocious baby whose shrewd behavior began virtually at birth. When he was just a few hours old, Hermes walked out of the cave where he was born to see what was happening and to find something to do. It was said that he found a tortoise and constructed a lyre out of its shell. Shortly thereafter, Hermes stole some of the cattle belonging to his brother Apollo. He managed to gain Apollo's forgiveness by giving him the lyre he had just invented. All this was believed to have happened before Hermes was twenty-four hours old!

Hermes acquired his place on Mount Olympus by cleverly creating a role for himself. He became the messenger to the gods and was useful and quite indispensable. Although he was best known as the messenger to the gods, he was also revered as the protector of travelers on earth and as the guide of souls on their journey to the Lower World. Perhaps as a result of his early experiences in which he traded a lyre for forgiveness, Hermes became extremely skilled at negotiation. He was worshipped as the god of commerce and market and was known, from time to time, to have resorted to a white lie or bit of cunning to achieve his goals.

[1] **pinnacle:** high peak
[2] **vulnerable:** open to temptation
[3] **implacable:** unyielding; not able to be pacified
[4] **dallied:** played at love
[5] **venerated:** treated with reverence
[6] **scourge:** cause of calamity or affliction
[7] **carnage:** slaughter or massacre
[8] **vultures:** hawklike birds of prey which thrive on dead flesh
[9] **transgression:** wrongdoing
[10] **beguiling:** charming
[11] **emulate:** try to equal
[12] **rebuffed:** bluntly rejected

A CLOSER LOOK

1. Answer the following for each of the gods and goddesses described in this section. What were the strengths and weaknesses of the particular god or goddess? What role did he or she play in the mythology of the ancient world?

2. Of the various gods and goddesses on Mount Olympus, which would you most like to meet? Which do you think you would like best? Which would you like least? Explain and give reasons for your answers.

GODS OF OLYMPUS

Greek Name	Latin Name	Domain	Symbols
Zeus	Jupiter or Jove	supreme ruler of the gods, god of the sky and heavens	thunderbolt, oak, eagle
Hera	Juno	queen of the gods, patroness of married women	peacock, cow
Poseidon	Neptune	god of the sea, god of horses and horsemanship	trident, horse
Hades or Pluto	Pluto or Dis	god of the underworld, god of wealth	Cerberus (his three-headed dog)
Ares	Mars	god of war	spear, burning torch, vultures, dogs
Athena or Pallas Athena	Minerva	goddess of wisdom, goddess of weaving, goddess of war	aegis, owl, olive tree shield
Artemis	Diana	goddess of the moon, supreme huntress, protectress of maidens	stag, cypress, arrows
Hestia	Vestia	goddess of the home and hearth	hearth fire
Aphrodite	Venus	goddess of love and beauty	dove, sparrow, swan myrtle tree
Hephaestus	Vulcan	god of fire, god of metal, workers, workman of the gods	forge, anvil
Apollo or Phoebus Apollo	Apollo	god of the sun, god of medicine, god of music and poetry	sun chariot, lyre, laurel
Hermes	Mercury	messenger of the gods, god of commerce	winged shoes, winged hat, Caduceus (wand)

From the Myths

THE STORY OF IO

● Because Zeus was immortal, he was able to pursue his varous loves in most unusual and creative ways. His wife, Hera, a goddess as well as a jealous woman, employed many fantastic strategies to keep her wandering husband in line. Io, a lovely young princess, found out most painfully what it was like to incur the love of Zeus and the wrath of Hera all at the same time.

I O, A BEAUTIFUL YOUNG PRINCESS, CAUGHT THE EYE of Zeus who, as frequently happened, was quite unable to resist the lure of an attractive maiden. Hera, always the jealous wife (and with good reason), grew very suspicious. One day, when Hera was just about to catch her husband and Io together, Zeus commanded a tremendous cloud to surround the earth and conceal his activities. Hera was not fooled. She knew perfectly well that the sudden darkness was not a natural occurrence, and that her husband was up to no good.

Hera quickly ordered the cloud to vanish, and it did. But Zeus was even quicker. By the time the cloud lifted, Zeus had turned Io into a lovely black and white heifer.[1] There he stood, not with a mortal maiden, but with a cow. When Hera asked her husband about the heifer, he told her that he had never seen the creature until just that very moment when she emerged newborn from the earth. Again, Hera was not fooled. She knew that the spotted creature was not a simple beast of the field.

"I've never seen such a fine and lovely heifer," Hera cooed to Zeus in the sweetest of tones. "I simply must have her for my very own."

Zeus found himself in a most difficult predicament.[2] Were he to refuse his wife the heifer, then the entire tale would be revealed at once. What excuse could he use to deny Hera her request? He could think of none. So, with sorrow and reluctance, Zeus turned Io over to certain misery.

Hera knew precisely how to keep Io away from Zeus. She put Argus, who had one hundred eyes, in charge of her. Argus was an ideal watchman because while some eyes slept, others watched. Io was wretchedly unhappy, and Zeus had no way to help her. Finally Zeus asked his son Hermes to help. Hermes, the messenger of the gods, had always been exceedingly clever.

It wasn't long before Hermes concocted a plan to outwit Argus. Hermes began by telling stories to Argus. The stories were designed to be tiresome, and so they were. One by one, the eyes of Argus closed. When all the eyes were shut, Hermes killed Argus immediately. Hera, much distraught over the loss of Argus, placed his eyes in the peacock's tail, where they remain even today.

But the tale of the cheating husband, the girl turned into a cow, and the watchman with the hundred eyes did not end with the peacock's tail. Hera, who was not yet finished with Io, sent a gadfly with a swordlike stinger to follow Io and inflict perpetual [3] torment. Finally Io swam across the sea (now named the Ionian Sea in her honor) to Egypt. When she reached the Nile, Zeus was able to conceal her from Hera and return the girl to human form. Io bore Zeus a son named Epaphus, who was said to have become the king of Egypt and father of Libya.

[1] **heifer:** a young cow
[2] **predicament:** an unpleasantly difficult situation
[3] **perpetual:** continuing forever

A CLOSER LOOK

1. Why did Zeus change Io into a heifer? What caused Hera to be suspicious of what her husband had done?

2. Do you think Io deserved the punishment Hera inflicted on her? Why, or why not?

III. Myths of Nature

For as long as there have been humans on earth, it is likely that questions have been asked about various aspects of nature. Why does the lightning flash and the thunder roar? Why does the sun seem to travel across the sky each day? Why are some places deserts, some green fields, and still others ice-covered year round? Why do the seasons come and go? Why and what is the wind? Early people, in the days before scientific research as we now know it, had to invent the answers to questions such as these.

Many of the ancient myths resulted from efforts by creative and thoughtful humans to answer questions they had about the world around them. The thunderbolt and its accompanying lightning flash, for example, were attributed to the whims and temper of Zeus. Apollo, the sun god, was said to carry the sun across the sky each day in his chariot. The scorched deserts were believed to have resulted from the time Apollo's son, Phaethon, drove the sun chariot too close to the earth. For each natural phenomenon the ancient Greeks and Romans had a story or perhaps several stories which offered an explanation.

While many of the great immortal gods of the heavens were mischievous and somewhat troublesome to humans at best, and downright destructive at worst, the two great gods of the earth—Demeter (Ceres), goddess of corn, and Dionysius (Bacchus), god of wine—were good and faithful friends of humankind. These two gods represented the gifts of the earth and the bounty of the harvest. And they, like humans, experienced sorrow during the winter until spring came again each year.

Pan, the son of Hermes, was a god who lived in the thickets and woodlands of the earth. Pan, who had the head and torso of a human, was usually depicted with the horns and hooves of a goat. The earth was also believed to be inhabited by numerous minor deities called nymphs, who were associated with nature in various ways.

Aille X. West

PHAETHON: SON OF THE SUN

● The ancient Greeks and Romans often used myths to explain natural happenings they didn't fully understand. For example, they believed the rising and setting of the sun to be caused by the sun god, who was believed to drive the sun through the heavens each day in a chariot pulled by strong horses. This was no easy task, as you'll find out in the myth that follows.

PHAETHON'S FATHER, APOLLO, WAS THE GOD OF the sun. Once when Phaethon was boasting to friends about his father, the lad was severely challenged by his listeners. "You are not truly a son of the sun," one companion taunted. "That's just a story your mother made up to satisfy the curious and impress those who know no better."

Phaethon grew angry, first at those who doubted his story and then at himself for being unable to prove he was right. He went to his mother, Clymene, and related how he—and she—had been insulted in such a demeaning way. "If I am truly a son of Apollo," the boy begged, "give me some sign of its truth so that we may be insulted no more."

Clymene was so furious her word had been questioned that she turned to the sun and cried out, "I swear by the flames of the sun itself that he is truly your father. If what I say be not the truth, then may my eyes never see the light again."

Then Clymene turned to Phaethon. "But you need not take my oath as proof. You can easily find your father's place in the east at dawn. Go there and ask him yourself."

Phaethon dashed off to find the proof of his pedigree he so desired.

He approached the great palace in the east, but was so dazzled by the light that he could not bear to draw too near as he faced his father.

"Phaethon, my son," spoke Apollo. "Why have you journeyed so long and far to visit me? What is it that you wish?"

And Phaethon replied, "Oh sun, great light of the earth, tell me that you are really my father, and I truly your son. Give me some proof that I might convince my disbelieving friends. Banish all doubts from my mind. Defend the honor of my mother."

"You are truly my son, Phaethon. And as a token of proof, I shall give you a gift—any one gift you wish. You need only ask."

The god of the sun had hardly finished speaking when Phaethon made known his desired gift. "Let me, for just one day," the boy said, "drive the great horses that carry the sun through the skies."

Apollo was instantly sorry that he had promised his son the choice of a gift. "Anything but that, my son," the great god of light said in a voice touched with pleading and sadness, and a bit of fear for what was to come. "None but myself can control these steeds with their fiery burden. The road at its beginning is very steep, and the horses must struggle to make their way. They are, to be sure, freshest in the morning, but still a strong hand is required to guide them. By noon, when the chariot is at its highest point, the distance from earth is so great that even I have been somewhat dizzied by the height. And the downhill plunge of afternoon requires a steady hand and great strength to keep the horses on course and under control. It is too much for you, my son," Apollo went on. "Ask me for anything else, but not this."

"No, father, you gave your word that I might have the gift of my choice as proof of who I am. I choose to have the chariot with the sun for one day in your place. If you are truly my father, you will honor your word to me."

And so, Apollo, with grieving heart, agreed to keep his promise. The horses were harnessed to the chariot, and the sun god gave his offspring a few last words of instruction. "Do not make your own way through the heavens," he told Phaethon. "You will see the wheel tracks I have made in my daily rounds, and you should follow them as closely as you are able. Keep your hands firmly on the reins, and above all, don't use the whip or otherwise urge the horses on. Your most arduous[1] task will be to keep the team in hand."

"Enough, father," said the brash young man. "I can manage. For, after all, am I not your son? Who better could take your place?" And the lad, impatient to begin his adventure, didn't want to wait to hear further directives. On deaf ears went the father's caution to keep high above the earth so as not to scorch it, but not so high that the sun burned the houses of the gods. The advice to avoid dangerous constellations—the Serpent, for example, and the great Crab—likewise went unheard.

Phaethon leaped into the chariot and eagerly took the reins. The horses tore off instantly at the boy's bidding. Faster and faster they galloped, for they barely noticed the boy's light weight in the chariot. Phaethon's hands—unaccustomed to the pull of headstrong steeds— were not equal to the task of exerting control.

Apollo, knowing that disaster was racing through the heavens in that chariot, broke down and wept openly. He had kept his word and his honor, and had lost his son. Phaethon, meanwhile, could barely breathe as the horses sped through the skies at their pleasure. The boy could neither steer nor stop, and the animals went where they wished.

From time to time, as the steeds turned earthward, they left behind them deserts and wasteland where once had been green fields. Great fires that destroyed whole towns were set by the sun's rays as they strayed out of the chariot close to the earth's surface. Realizing that the entire earth could be consumed by fire, Apollo turned to Zeus, king of the gods for assistance.

Zeus struck Phaethon from the chariot with a thunderbolt, and the lad fell earthward. As he plummeted[2] headlong from the sky like a shooting star, Phaethon's flaming hair and garments streaked the air with light. The great river Eridanus, now known as the river Po in Italy, received the flaming frame of Phaethon and gave him a watery grave. Phaethon's sisters, the Heliades, lamented his loss. Their weeping showered the river bank, and they were turned into poplar trees. It was said that their tears continued to flow and were turned into amber.

The storm sent by Zeus darkened the skies and cooled the sun long enough for Apollo to capture his horses and corral them until the next day.

Apollo was saddened by the loss of his son, but grateful to Zeus for sparing the rest of the earth. And from that day on, the ancient peoples used the story of Phaethon to explain why the world had deserts and people with sun-darkened skin.

[1] **arduous:** difficult
[2] **plummeted:** plunged

A CLOSER LOOK

1. Why did Phaethon feel the need to go to Apollo? Do you think he should have done so? What do you think you or your friends might do in a similar situation? Explain and give reasons for your response.

2. Why did Apollo do what he did when Phaethon came to him? Do you think he made the correct choice under the circumstances? Why, or why not?

3. What natural phenomena did the ancient Greeks and Romans use the story of Phaethon to explain?

Charles Mills Gayley

MYTH OF MINERVA AND ARACHNE

● The myth of the goddess Minerva (Athena) involving an imprudent challenge made by a mortal, Arachne, has been beautifully retold by Charles Mills Gayley, an eminent scholar in the field of language and literature. The ancient Greeks used the story of Minerva and Arachne to explain the perpetual efforts of the spider to spin a web.

THE GODDESS MINERVA PEACEFULLY COMPETED with Neptune for claim to the city of Athens. During the reign of the first king of Athens, the two deities had contended for possession of the city. The gods decreed that it should be awarded to the one who produced the gift most useful to mortals. Neptune gave the horse. Minerva produced the olive. The gods awarded the city to the goddess, and after her Greek appellation, Athena, it was named.

In another contest, a mortal dared to come into competition with the grey-eyed daughter of Jove. This was Arachne, a maiden who had attained such skill in the arts of carding and spinning, of weaving and embroidery, that the Nymphs themselves would leave their groves and fountains to come and gaze upon her work. It was not only beautiful when it was done, but beautiful also in the doing. To watch her one would have said that Minerva herself had taught her. But this she denied, and could not bear to be thought a pupil even of a goddess. "Let Minerva try her skill with mine," said she. "If beaten, I will pay the penalty." Minerva heard this and was displeased. Assuming the form of an old woman, she appeared to Arachne and kindly advised her to challenge her fellow mortals if she would, but at once to ask forgiveness of the goddess. Arachne bade the old dame to keep her counsel for others. "I am not afraid of the goddess; let her try her skill, if she dare venture."

"She comes," said Minerva, and dropping her disguise, stood confessed. The Nymphs bent low in homage and all the bystanders paid reverence. Arachne alone was unterrified. A sudden color dyed her cheek, and then she grew pale; but she stood to her resolve and rushed on her fate.

They proceed to the contest. Each takes her station and attaches the web to the beam. Then the slender shuttle is passed in and out among the threads. The reed with its fine teeth strikes up the woof into his place and compacts the web. Wool of Tyrian dye is contrasted with that of other colors, shaded off into one another so adroitly[1] that the joining deceives the eye. And the effect is like the bow whose long arch tinges the heavens, formed by sunbeams reflected from the shower, in which, where the colors meet they seem as one, but at a little distance from the point of contact are wholly different.

Minerva wove the scene of her contest with Neptune (Poseidon). Twelve of the heavenly powers were represented, Jupiter, with august[3] gravity, sitting in the midst. Neptune, the ruler of the sea, held his trident and appeared to have just smitten the earth, from which a horse had leaped forth. The bright-eyed goddess depicted herself with helmed head, her aegis[4] covering her breast, as when she had created the olive tree with its berries and its dark green leaves.

> Amongst these leaves she made a Butterfly,
>   With excellent device and wondrous slight,
> Fluttering among the olives wantonly,
>   That seemed to live, so like it was in sight;
> The velvet nap which on his wings doth lie,
>   The silken down with which his back is dight,
> His broad outstretchèd horns, his hairy thighs,
> His glorious colors, and his glistening eyes.
>
> Which when Arachne saw, as overlaid
>   And masterèd with workmanship so rare,
> She stood astonished long, ne aught, gainsaid;
>   And with fast-fixèd eyes on her did stare.

From Spenser's Muiopotmos

So wonderful was the central circle of Minerva's web; and in the four corners were represented incidents illustrating the displeasure of the gods at such presumptuous mortals as had dared to contend with them. These were meant as warnings from Minerva to her rival to give up the contest before it was too late.

But Arachne did not yield. She filled her web with subjects designedly chosen to exhibit the failings and errors of the gods. One scene represented Leda caressing the swan; and another, Danaë and the golden shower. Still another depicted Europa deceived by Jupiter under the disguise of a bull. Its appearance was that of a real bull, so naturally was it wrought and so natural the water in which it swam.

With such subjects Arachne filled her canvas, wonderfully well done but strongly marking her presumption and impiety.[5] Minerva could not forebear to admire, yet was indignant at the insult. She struck the web with her shuttle and rent it to pieces; then, touching the forehead of Arachne, she made her realize her guilt.

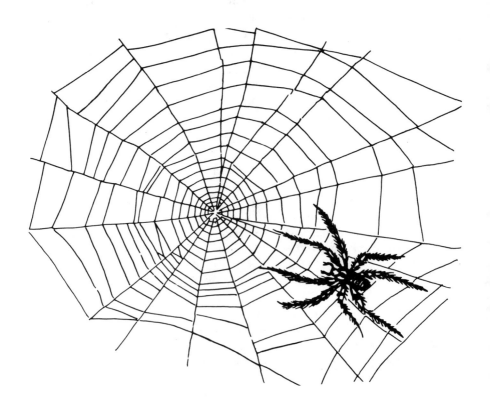

It was more than mortal could bear; and forthwith Arachne hanged herself. "Live, guilty woman," said Minerva, "but that thou mayest preserve the memory of this lesson continue to hang, both thou and thy descendants, to all future times." Then, sprinkling her with the juices of aconite, the goddess transformed her into a spider, forever spinning the thread by which she is suspended.

[1] **adroitly:** skillfully
[2] **august:** dignified
[3] **aegis:** shield containing the head of Medusa
[4] **presumptuous:** too bold
[5] **impiety:** lack of proper respect

A CLOSER LOOK

1. Why did Minerva disguise herself as an old woman and confront Arachne? What was Arachne's response? What do you think the young woman should have done? Why?

2. What did Minerva's scene contain? What message did she intend for her rival? How did Arachne react?

3. What did Arachne's scene contain? How did Minerva react? What happened to Arachne?

Bernard and Dorothy Evslin, and Ned Hoopes

ECHO AND NARCISSUS

● The story of Echo and Narcissus is a nature myth the ancient Greeks used to explain why there were echoes, and how the flower known as narcissus came to be. Like so many of the ancient stories, this myth reveals as much about humankind as it does about phenomena of nature.

OF ALL THE NYMPHS OF RIVER AND WOOD, A dryad named Echo was the best beloved. She was not only very beautiful and very kind, but had a haunting musical voice. The other dryads and naiads and creatures of the wood begged her to sing to them and tell them stories—and she did. She was a great favorite of Aphrodite who used to come all the way from Olympus to chat with Echo and listen to her tales. Being goddess of love, she was especially concerned with gossip—which is mostly about who loves whom and what they are doing about it. And Echo kept her entertained as no one else could.

Aphrodite said, "All the world asks me for favors, Echo. But not you. Tell me, is there not someone you would wish to love you? Some man, boy, god? Just name him, and I will make him fall madly in love with you."

But Echo laughed, and said, "Alas, sweet Aphrodite, I have seen no man who pleases me. And gods are too fickle.[1] Man and boy—I look at

46

them all very carefully, but none seems beautiful enough to match my secret dream. When the time comes, I shall ask for your help—if it ever comes."

"Well, you are lovely enough to demand the best," said Aphrodite. "On the other hand, the best happens only once. And who can wait so long? However, I am always at your service."

Now Echo did not know this, but at that moment the most beautiful boy in the whole world was lost in that very wood, trying to find his way out. His name was Narcissus, and he was so handsome that he had never been able to speak to any woman except his mother. For any girl who saw him immediately fainted. Of course this also gave him a very high opinion of himself. And, as he went through the woods, he thought:

"Oh, how I wish I could find someone as beautiful as I. I will not be friends with anything less perfect in face or form. Why should I? This leaves me lonely, true, but it's better than lowering myself."

So he walked along the path, but he was going the wrong way, getting more and more lost. In the other part of the wood Echo had just said farewell to Aphrodite, and was coming back to the hollow tree in which she lived. She came to a glade in the forest, and there saw something that made her gasp in astonishment, and hide behind a tree. For whom did she see but Zeus himself—king of the gods, lord of the sky. He was leaning on his volt-blue lightning shaft, holding a river nymph by the shoulder, and she was smiling up at him.

"Well," said Echo, "He's at it again. Won't Aphrodite enjoy hearing about *this*!"

But then her attention was caught by something else. She turned to see a tall purple-clad figure moving through the trees toward the glade. She recognized Hera, queen of the gods, jealous wife of Zeus, and she realized that Hera must have heard of what Zeus was doing, and was coming to catch him. And so the kind-hearted nymph hurried forward and curtsied low before Hera, saying, "Greetings, great queen. Welcome to the wood."

"Hush, fool!" whispered Hera. "Don't say a word! I am trying to take someone by surprise."

"This is a proud day for us," said Echo, thinking swiftly, "to be visited by many gods. Just two minutes ago, Zeus was here looking for you."

"Zeus? Looking for *me*? Are you sure?"

"The great Zeus. Your husband. He asked me whether I had seen you. Said he had heard you were coming this way, and he wished very much

to meet you. When I told him I had not seen you, he flew off looking
very disappointed."

"Really? Can it be so? Zeus looking for me? Disappointed? Well—
miracles never cease. Which way did he go?"

"Oh . . . toward Olympus."

"Thank you, child," said Hera. "I'll be going too."

And she disappeared.

In the meantime, Zeus, hearing voices, had hidden himself and the
river nymph in the underbrush. When Hera left, he came out, and to
thank Echo he gave her a shining blue sapphire ring from his own finger.

Hera, having returned to Olympus, found that Zeus was not there.

48

She realized that something was wrong, and sped back to the forest. The first thing she saw was Echo admiring a large sapphire ring that burned on her finger like a fallen star. Hera recognized the ring, and immediately understood that the nymph had tricked her in some way and had been given the ring as a reward.

"Wretched creature!" she cried. "I know what you have done. I see the gift you have been given. And I would not have it said that my husband is more generous than I. So I too shall reward you for what you have done. Because you have used your voice for lying, you shall never be able to say anything to anyone again—except the last words that have been said to you. Now, try lying."

"Try lying," said Echo.

"No more shall you meddle in high concerns—no more shall you gossip and tell stories and sing songs—but endure this punishment evermore . . . "

"Evermore . . . " said Echo, sobbing.

And Hera went away to search for Zeus. And the nymph, weeping, rushed toward her home in the hollow tree. As she was going she saw once again the dazzling brightness that was the face of a god, and she stopped to see. It was no god, but a lad about her own age, with black hair and eyes the color of the sapphire Zeus had given her. When she saw him, all the grief of her punishment dissolved, and she was full of great laughing joy. For here was the boy she had been looking for all her life, as beautiful as her secret dream . . . a boy she could love.

She danced toward him. He stopped and said, "Pardon me, but can you show me a path out of the wood?"

"Out of the wood . . . " said Echo.

"Yes," he said. I'm lost. I've been wandering for hours, and I can't seem to find my way out of the wood."

"Out of the wood . . . "

"Yes. I've told you twice. I'm lost. Can you help me find the way?"

"The way . . . "

"Are you deaf, perhaps? Why must I repeat everything?"

"Repeat everything . . . "

"No, I will not! It's a bore! I won't do it!"

"Do it . . . "

"Look I can't stand here arguing with you. If you don't want to show me the way, well then, I'll just try to find someone who can."

"Who can . . . "

Narcissus glared at her, and started away. But she came to him, and put her arms around him, and tried to kiss his face.

"Oh no—none of that!" said Narcissus, shoving her away. "You're just like all the rest of them, aren't you? They faint, and you say stupid things. Stop it! You can't kiss me."

"Kiss me..."

"No!"

"No..."

And she tried to kiss him again. Again he pushed her aside. She fell on her knees on the path, and hugged his legs, and lifted her lovely tear-streaked face to his, trying to speak. But she could not.

"No!" he said. "Let go! You can't hold me here. I will not love you."

"Love you..."

He tore himself from her grip and strode away. "Farewell," he cried.

"Farewell..."

She looked after him until he disappeared. And when he was gone she felt such sadness, such terrible tearing grief, such pain in every part of her, that it seemed she was being torn apart by white-hot little pincers, torn flesh from bone. And since she could not speak, she said this prayer to herself:

"Oh, Aphrodite... fair goddess... you promised me a favor. Do me one now. Hear me though I am voiceless. My love has disappeared, and I must disappear too, for I cannot bear the pain."

And Aphrodite, in the garden on Olympus, heard this prayer—for prayers do not have to be spoken to be heard. She looked down upon the grieving nymph, and pitied her, and made her disappear. Her body melted into thin cool air, so that the pain was gone. All was gone... except her voice, for Aphrodite could not bear to lose the sound of that lovely story-telling voice. The goddess said, "I grant you your wish— and one thing more. You have not asked vengeance[2] upon the love that has betrayed you. You are too sweet and kind. I shall take vengeance, nevertheless. I decree now that whoever has caused you this pain will know the same terrible longing. He will fall in love with someone who cannot return his love... and will forever desire and never achieve."

But Narcissus knew nothing of this—of Echo's grief, nor Aphrodite's vow. He wandered the forest path, thinking, "All these girls who love me on sight—it's too bad I cannot find one as beautiful as I. For until I do, I shall not love. And all their loving will be only the vexation[3] to me."

He sat down on the bank of a river to rest. Not a river really, but a finger of the river—a clear little stream moving slowly through rocks. The sun shone on it; it became a mirror, holding the trees and the sky upside down, and a small silver trembling sun. And Narcissus, looking into the stream, saw a face.

He blinked his eyes, and looked again. It was still there—the most beautiful face he had ever seen. As beautiful, he knew, as his own, but with a nimbus[4] of light behind it so that the hair was blurred and looked long—like a girl's. He gazed and gazed, and could not have enough of it. He knew that he could look upon this face forever and still not be satisfied. He put out his hand to touch her. The water trembled, and she disappeared.

"A water nymph," he thought. "A lovely dryad . . . daughter of the river god, no doubt. The loveliest of his daughters. She is shy. Like me, she can't bear to be touched. Ah . . . here she is again."

The face looked at him out of the stream. Again, very timidly, he reached his hand. Again the water trembled and the face disappeared.

"I will stay here until she loves me," he said to himself. "She may hide now, but presently she will recognize me too. And come out." And he said aloud: "Come out, lovely one."

And the voice of Echo, who had followed him to the stream, said, "Lovely one . . . "

"Hear that, hear that!" cried Narcissus, overjoyed. "She cares for me too. You do, don't you? You love me."

"Love me . . . "

"I do . . . I do . . . Finally I have found someone to love. Come out, come out . . . Oh, will you never come out?"

"Never come out . . . " said Echo.

"Don't say that, please don't say that. Because I will stay here till you do. This, I vow."

"I vow . . . "

"Your voice is beautiful as your face. And I will stay here, adoring you forever."

"Forever . . . "

And Narcissus stayed there, leaning over the stream, watching the face in the water, watching, watching, watching . . . sometimes pleading with it to come out, hearing its voice answer. Coaxing, begging, looking. . . . Day after day he stayed there, night after night, never moving, never eating, never looking away from the face. He stayed there so long that his legs grew into the bank of the river, and became roots. His hair grew long and leafy. And his pale face and blue eyes became delicate blue and white petals—the flower Narcissus, that lives on the riverbank, and leans over watching its reflection in the water.

And there you can find it till this day. And in the woods too, when all is still, you will sometimes come upon Echo. And if you call to her in a certain way, she will answer your call.

[1] **fickle:** likely to change
[2] **vengeance:** just punishment
[3] **vexation:** irritation or annoyance
[4] **nimbus:** cloud

A CLOSER LOOK

1. Why did Aphrodite enjoy Echo's company? Do you think Echo would have been an entertaining companion? Why, or why not?

2. What did Echo do that made Hera angry? What do you think Echo should have done in that situation? Why do you think so?

3. What sort of a person was Narcissus? Do you think he got what he deserved? Do you think Echo was fairly treated? Explain and give reasons for your answers.

From the Myths

THE TWO GODS OF THE EARTH

● It has been said that the immortal gods were not only of little use to humans but that these gods quite frequently caused harm by their unpredictable ways. There were, however, two exceptions: Demeter (Ceres) and Dionysius (Bacchus). These two great gods of the earth were especially kind and useful to human beings.

DEMETER (KNOWN IN LATIN AS CERES) AND Dionysius (also known as Bacchus) were humankind's best friends among the gods. Demeter, a daughter of Cronus and Rhea, was the Goddess of Corn. She looked after all the green things of the earth including plants, trees, and especially the crops planted in fields. Bacchus was the God of Wine.

Demeter was the older of the two. Cornfields came long before vineyards in the scheme of things, and fields in which crops were sowed were evidence of the earliest human settlements. The divinity honored for the harvest was a goddess rather than a god, because it was the women of the ancient peoples who tended the fields. The men of the earliest civilizations were hunters and fighters, while the women were responsible for home, hearth, and agriculture. Demeter, as Goddess of Agriculture, was an important role model for the women of the Ancient world.

Demeter was the mother of Persephone, an only daughter who was carried off by Hades, God of the Underworld. (See the story of Hades and Persephone on page 66.) After the loss of her daughter, in inconsolable[1] grief Demeter withheld her gifts from the earth. Nothing thrived, and the earth became barren and cold. Eventually Persephone

was permitted to join those in the upper world for all but the winter months. Demeter again nourished the earth with her gifts and life flourished. Each year, however, the earth became cold and nothing grew during the time Persephone returned to Hades for the winter months and her sorrowful mother refused to bless the fields.

Dionysius (Bacchus), the God of Wine, was responsible for the vineyards which played such an important part in ancient agriculture. Dionysius was also worshipped as the God of Vegetation. He loved the woodlands and hillsides which were rich in shrubs and trees.

Dionysius, like so many others, was a son of Zeus and a mortal woman. The mother of Dionysius was Semele, the beautiful daughter of Cadmus, King of Thebes. Zeus was so captivated by Semele that he promised her any wish, and he swore by the River Styx.

Semele asked Zeus to prove his identity and his love by coming to her arrayed in the full splendor of royal armor complete with thunderbolt.

Unfortunately for both Zeus and Semele, Zeus had to do what he had sworn to do. Although Zeus knew that Semele would be unable to survive the heat and light that would accompany him and his thunderbolt, he had sworn on the River Styx to grant any one wish Semele requested. No one, not even the supreme god of Mount Olympus, could avoid keeping an oath made in that way. Hera, always the jealous wife, influenced Semele's choice of wish by encouraging the young maiden to question the authenticity[2] of her lover's immortality. When Zeus appeared in his godlike form to Semele, the heat and light were so intense that Semele was quickly turned to ashes. Zeus was able to save her unborn child, however, and this child became the god the Greeks knew as Dionysius.

Dionysius was attended by a rather unusual entourage.[3] He had many female followers who often expressed their adoration in a frenzied[4] way. He was also accompanied by creatures which were half human and half beast such as satyrs, fauns, and sileni. Satyrs were shaggy creatures with ears, tail, and sometimes the horns and hooves of a goat, but the body of a man. Fauns and sileni looked mostly like humans, but they had the ears and sometimes the tail of an animal.

Various stories about Dionysius present conflicting views about what the god was like. In some he is described as a comrade and bringer of joy. In others he is revealed as brutal and savage. When Dionysius went to Thebes with his group of excited followers, King Pentheus decided that this weird assortment of characters should be punished. Pentheus, unaware that Dionysius was both his cousin and a god, ignored warnings to honor the visitor. Dionysius retaliated by causing those closest to Pentheus to become temporarily insane and to destroy the king.

The ancient Greeks appeared to understand quite well why the God of Wine would behave in ways that were not consistent. They realized wine was a cause of drunkenness as well as a source of pleasure. Dionysius exemplified the negative aspects of drinking as well as the cheer.

[1] **inconsolable:** not able to be comforted
[2] **authenticity:** genuineness
[3] **entourage:** group of followers
[4] **frenzied:** excited in a frantic way

A CLOSER LOOK

1. Why was the deity of agriculture a goddess rather than a god? Do you think such a choice would be likely in today's world? Why, or why not?

2. How did the ancient people explain the occurrence of winter each year?

3. What lesson about life can be learned from Dionysius, the God of Wine?

From the Myths

PAN

● Pan was a god of nature who lived on earth, not on Mount Olympus. He was often thought of as the chief of the numerous creatures which inhabited the wild places of the world.

IN NATURE, PAN WAS CONSIDERED THE CHIEF OF THE gods living in the world. He inhabited the woodlands and other wild places, traveling about and making merry. Pan was the son of Hermes, and he was generally a noisy and merry creature. He was generally depicted as being part animal, with the horns and hooves of a goat and the body of a man.

Pan was a musician, and he played melodious tunes on his pipes of reed. Pan fell in love with many a nymph, but his strange appearance seemed to put them off, and he was inevitably faced with rejection. He was persistent, however, and always tried again.

Many of the pleasant melodies of the woods were attributed to Pan. Some sounds, particularly night sounds in the wilderness, that may have frightened people were also attributed to this god. A traveller alone in the wilderness who was suddenly terrified by such sounds was said to experience "panic" because the cause of his fear could be traced to Pan.

> Great Nature had a million words,
> In tongues of bees and songs of birds,
> But none to breathe the heart of man,
> Till music filled the pipes o' Pan.
>
> Henry van Dyke

A CLOSER LOOK

1. Why did the nymphs reject Pan's advances? Do you think they were right to do so? Why, or why not?

2. Imagine that you were travelling alone through the woodlands of ancient Greece on a dark night. Described the sights and sounds you might encounter. Why do you think the ancient people attributed certain of the sounds to Pan?

3. What does the word "panic" mean? What did the god Pan have to do with the origin of this word?

Elizabeth Barrett Browning

A MUSICAL INSTRUMENT

What was he doing, the great god Pan,
  Down in the reeds by the river?
Spreading ruin and scattering ban,
Splashing and paddling with hoofs of a goat,
And breaking the golden lilies afloat
  With the dragon-fly on the river?

He tore out a reed, the great god Pan,
  From the deep cool bed of the river,
The limpid water turbidly ran,
And the broken lilies a-dying lay,
And the dragon-fly had fled away,
  Ere he brought it out of the river.

High on the shore sat the great god Pan,
  While turbidly flowed the river,
And hacked and hewed as a great god can
With his hard bleak steel at the patient reed,
Till there was not a sign of the leaf indeed
  To prove it fresh from the river.

He cut it short, did the great god Pan,
  (How tall it stood in the river!)
Then drew the pith, like the heart of a man,
Steadily from the outside ring,
And notched the poor dry empty thing
  In holes as he sat by the river.

"This is the way," laughed the great god Pan
  (Laughed while he sat by the river),
"The only way since gods began
To make sweet music, they could succeed."
Then dropping his mouth to a hole in the reed,
  He blew in power by the river.

Sweet, sweet, sweet, O Pan!
  Piercing sweet by the river!
Blinding sweet, O great god Pan!
The sun on the hill forgot to die,
And the lilies revived, and the dragon-fly
  Came back to dream on the river.

Yet half a beast is the great god Pan
  To laugh, as he sits by the river,
Making a poet out of a man:
The true gods sigh for the cost and pain—
For the reed which grows nevermore again
  As a reed with the reeds of the river.

IV. Myths of the Underworld

Hades (Pluto) and his Queen, Persephone (Proserpine), governed the underworld, or kingdom of the dead. That place, a region of darkness believed by the ancients to be inhabited by the spirits of the dead, was often referred to by the name of its ruler, Hades. According to Homers's *Iliad,* Hades "lay beneath the secret places of the earth." In the *Odyssey,* Homer suggested that the way to Hades was across the river Oceanus, at the underside of the very limits of the known world. Later poets referred to passages from the earth to Hades near deep lakes or through caverns.

Hades was sometimes described as divided into sections, although many stories did not distinguish between the underworld regions. The area where the dead passed shortly after death was sometimes referred to as Erebus, a name which was occasionally used interchangeably with Hades. The deepest underworld region was known as Tartarus, in some instances described as a dire and dreadful place to which the gods sent those whom they wished to punish. At other times, however, the name Tartarus was used instead of Hades to refer to the entire lower region of the underworld, and not simply the place where the unfavored dead were imprisoned in misery. The Elysian Fields, or Elysium, was a region of the underworld like paradise, to which those especially favored by the gods might be sent.

Five rivers were believed to separate the underworld from the earth above. The Acheron, known as the river of woe, poured down into Cocytus, the river of wailing and lamentation. The Styx was the sacred river by which the gods took their oaths which could not be broken. The Lethe was the river of forgetfulness, and the Phlegethon was a river of fire.

The souls of the dead were carried by boat to Hades by Charon, an aged ferryman who carried only those whose passage had been paid in advance by the placement of a coin on the tongue prior to burial. The gate to Hades was guarded by a dreadful three-headed, dragon-tailed dog named Cerberus. All were permitted to enter the underworld, but Cerberus allowed no one to leave.

From the Myths

THE LOWER WORLD

● Ancient peoples believed that the souls of the dead went to a mysterious world under the earth. Although they did not know what the place was really like, a look at the stories they told gives an idea of the Lower World as they imagined it to be.

THE REALM OF HADES WAS GLOOMY AND DARK, AND the sun never entered there. There was just enough dim light, however, to enable those in the Lower World to go about their business and recognize each other in the shadows. It was said that the people in Hades had pretty much the same appearance they had had on earth, although their bodies were but ghostly shadows without substance. It was also said that the beings in the Underworld could speak, although their voices were faint and ghostlike, and it was still possible for someone who had died to experience pain, both of body and mind.

As a person who had just died approached the River Styx, he or she would find the banks teeming[1] with a throng of countless other ghosts. The poet Virgil described the number of shades[2] awaiting passage across the Styx as comparable to the number of leaves that fall in the autumn. The waiting crowds were trying to board the boat that would take them across to Hades. Charon, the ferryman, stood by the boat. He

pushed back with his oar anyone who had not received the proper rites of burial or who could not pay the coin needed for the fare. Anyone rebuffed by Charon had to wait a century before trying again.

Across the river at the entrance to Hades stood Cerberus, a monstrous three-headed dog. Although his howling tended to terrify anyone who neared the gate, those who were entering Hades had nothing to fear. Cerberus let anyone pass once, on the way in. The animal was fiercely efficient, however, at preventing anyone from leaving.

Those who had died had to appear before judges who reviewed what had been done and what had been left undone in the earthly life above. This was necessary to assign each shade to the appropriate place in Hades. According to some storytellers and poets, those who had offended the gods or sinned egregiously[3] against their fellow humans on earth were likely to be sentenced to suffer in Tartarus. Those who were especially virtuous and deserving of reward were permitted to dwell happily in Elysium, the paradise of the Lower World. Those whose lives had been ordinary—not very good and not very bad—were destined to spend an eternity of aimless wandering in which they would know neither pain nor pleasure, just a tedious nothingness.

Tartarus was the part of Hades where punishment was administered to those who had sinned greatly. Some writers spoke of Tartarus as a great walled city into which no one could enter other than those sent by the gods to be punished. Other writers described Tartarus as a great hole—not unlike a seemingly bottomless pit—which descended into the depths as far below the earth's surface as the top of Mount Olympus rose above it.

Certain tales of punishment of mythological characters—Tantalus, Sisyphus, Ixion, and the Danaides, for example—have been retold and mentioned in literary works many times. Tantalus, a son of Zeus, lived in close touch with the gods, dined with them on Olympus, and shared in their secrets. Tantalus, however, betrayed the confidences of the gods and made the mistake of holding them up to ridicule. His eternal punishment in Tartarus was to have food and fresh water just before his eyes but always out of reach, and to have a great stone poised over his head as if about to fall. The hunger and thirst of Tantalus were desperate, and he was forever tempted but never satisfied.

Sisyphus was a king of Corinth who not only had angered Zeus, but who tried to evade his punishment through trickery and deceit. He even tried to escape from Hades. He failed, however, and was sentenced to roll a huge stone uphill. Each time he neared the top the stone slipped away and rolled back down. His labor, therefore, was never finished.

Ixion was a cruel and powerful king of Thessaly. It was said that he had designs on Hera, wife of Zeus. Ixion was so confident that Hera would look with favor on him that he boasted about his success. Zeus punished Ixion by having him bound to a wheel in Tartarus where he could suffer eternally while turning about and going nowhere.

The Danaides were the daughters of King Danaus. They were fifty in number. The brother of Danaus had fifty sons, and wished that the Danaides would become their wives. King Danaus objected, but could not prevent the arrangements from being made. He gave each one of the fifty daughters a dagger with which she could kill her husband on her wedding night. Forty-nine of the Danaides did as their father expected. They were condemned to Tartarus where their punishment was to gather water in a sieve[4] for all eternity. One daughter fell in love with her husband, achieved a happy life and escaped the punishment.

[1] **teeming:** abounding or swarming with something
[2] **shades:** ghosts (ghostly figures of those who have died)
[3] **egregiously:** in an extraordinarily or remarkably bad way
[4] **sieve:** a container with holes or a mesh in the bottom (used to strain liquids)

A CLOSER LOOK

1. What was the realm of Hades like? What did the ancient Greeks and Romans believe happened to those who had died? How do their views differ from your own beliefs or those of people you know?

2. Why was Tantalus sent to Tarturus to be punished? What was his punishment, and how did we get the word tantalize *from what happened to this particular son of Zeus?*

3. In what way were the punishments of Sisyphus, Ixion, and the Danaides similar? Do you think these punishments were suitable for the offenses involved? Why, or why not?

From the Myths

PERSEPHONE AND HADES

● Persephone, the lovely young daughter of Demeter, was picking flowers one day when the earth opened up and she disappeared. Her grieving mother finally found the girl in the underworld, where Hades had taken her to be his bride and queen.

PERSEPHONE (KNOWN TO THE ROMANS AS PROSERpine), was the daughter of Demeter (Ceres), goddess of the green things of the earth and the crops of the fields. One day Persephone was wandering through a sunny meadow picking flowers. She was particularly fond of daffodils, and her path took her hither and yon as she gathered a lovely bouquet.

Amidst the yellow daffodils, Persephone noticed a narcissus, a flower similar to a daffodil which she especially liked because of its sweet fragrance. As she bent to pick the flower, the ground began to open rapidly beneath her. Out of the huge crevice[1] thundered a team of powerful black horses pulling a chariot driven by Hades, the god of the Underworld himself.

Hades picked up Persephone in his strong arms, and pulled her into the chariot. In a matter of seconds, he had directed the horses back toward the Lower World, and the ground closed over the chariot, horses, and Persephone, removing them from sight of any living mortal.

Persephone's mother Demeter had been away at the time Hades emerged from the Lower World and abducted her daughter. The grieving mother searched far and wide but could find no trace of the girl.

Then she found out that Hades had taken Persephone to be his wife and queen. Demeter spent her time in deepest mourning for her lost child. She paid no attention to anything or anyone else. She failed to bless the fields, which lay fallow[2] and bare. Because nothing could grow, there was no harvest. Famine spread over the land.

Demeter asked Zeus for help. The supreme god knew that somehow Demeter would have to regain her daughter so that the flowers would bloom, the grain would grow again, and the earth and its people could survive. Zeus sent Hermes to tell Hades to send Persephone back to the land of the living. Zeus had told Demeter that the girl could return to earth as long as she had not eaten any food in Hades. Persephone, however, had already consumed some pomegranate[3] seeds. Zeus then arranged for Persephone to spend the winter months — one for each pomegranate seed she had eaten — in Hades, as Queen of the Underworld. He permitted her to spend spring, summer, and fall on earth. Each year, during the time Persephone is away, her mother grieves and nothing can grow. When Persephone returns each spring, the earth comes to life.

[1] **crevice:** a crack forming an opening
[2] **fallow:** (of land) left unseeded; uncultivated
[3] **pomegranate:** a segmented fruit with red rind and many seeds

A CLOSER LOOK

1. What was Persephone doing when Hades arrived and took her away? Why do you think Hades took the young woman in the way that he did?

2. Do you think Demeter was a typical mother? Why, or why not?

3. What did the ancient peoples attempt to explain using the story of Persephone and Hades? Why do you think they did so?

Ted Hughes

ORPHEUS

● Orpheus, son of Apollo, god of music, and the muse Calliope, was a famous musician of the ancient world whose musical ability surpassed even what one would expect of a child of such parents. When Orpheus played the lyre he captivated gods, mortals, and wild beasts alike. Even the trees in the forest and rocks in the fields swayed in time to his music.

Orpheus loved his wife Eurydice so deeply that when the bite of a viper killed her, Orpheus went to Hades to try to get her back. The music of Orpheus was so powerful that it even convinced the god of death to free Eurydice. There was one condition, however, which was that Orpheus could lead his wife out of Hades as long as he did not turn to look at her until they had reached the upper world.

Orpheus did look back, however, and Eurydice was lost to him forever.

Following is a modern version of the story of Orpheus and Eurydice, by the contemporary poet and playwright Ted Hughes.

Sweet singer, life-bringer Orpheus tries to buy his dead Eurydice with a magical song. Stones and hills are silent as Orpheus leaves earth to bargain with spider-faced Pluto who rules Death's kingdom with his maggot-faced wife, Persephone. As Orpheus plays, Persephone's pale face begins to open like a flower. Is a love song stronger than death?

Narrator: This is the story
Of Orpheus the Magician, whose magic was music.
(Popular music—guitar.)
This is the dance of the trees.
his music is so magic, he makes the trees dance.
The oaks unknot; they toss their limbs
And the willows whirl in a ring.
This is the dance of the trees.—*(Music stops. Giant sigh from all
    trees.)*
And this is the dance of the stones.
(Music for stones—still Pop.)
His music is so magic the stones dance.
The rocks uproot and caper in their places,
The pebbles skip like mice,
The ordinary stones bounce like footballs.
This is the dance of the stones.
(Music stops. Sigh from all stones.)
His music reaches up to the deer in the wrinkles of the hills.
(Deer music.)
It reaches down to the salmon in the pools below the falls.
(Salmon music.)
And wherever his music is heard, the dancing begins.
(Music)
His music has a name. Its name is happiness.

Every living thing loves Orpheus.
Because his music is happiness.
(*EURYDICE becomes visible.*)
And this is the cause of Orpheus' happiness:
This is his wife, for her he makes his music.
Orpheus: Why shouldn't I be happy?
The world is beautiful.
Day after day the huge gift of the world
Is beautiful as ever.
More beautiful than the whole world is my wife
Eurydice.
This is the secret of my music.
It is all for Eurydice, my happiness.
(*Music.*)
Narrator: Nevertheless, there keeps coming a voice to Orpheus—
a voice which he does not like.
Voice: Beware, Orpheus, beware.
Narrator: He dare not listen to the voice. He plays louder.
(*Music louder, to drown out the voice.*)
Narrator: Is it the voice of a bird? Or a spider? Or a serpent?
Voice (*very loud*): Beware, Orpheus, beware.
(*Music stops.*)
Voice (*very soft*): Beware, beware, beware.
Orpheus: What should I beware of? Why should I beware?
Voice: In the world of the trees,
In the world of the stones,
In the world of the frog, of the vole, of the linnet—
Every song has to be paid for.
Orpheus: Nonsense!
The world is a gift.
The brave take it with thanks and greet it with song.
Only the fearful peer at it with suspicion,
Thinking about the payment.
Voice: Beware, Orpheus, beware.
(*ORPHEUS drowns the voice with a storm of his music.*)
Narrator: Orpheus hammers his guitar nevertheless.
And the trees dance once again
And the stones dance.
The deer on the hills, and the salmon in the weirs
And the bears in the holes of the forest

And the travelers out on the roads
Dance, dance when they hear it.
The world dances with happiness.
But suddenly—
(*Music falters and stops.*)
Orpheus: My hand! Something has happened to my hand.
Narrator: Orpheus' hand suddenly becomes numb.
(*Sudden terrible cry in distance; voice coming nearer; a FRIEND bringing the news.*)
Friend: Orpheus! (*Nearer.*) Orpheus!
Orpheus: Who is that?
Friend (*nearer*): Orpheus!
Orpheus: Here.
Friend (*very close, entering*): Orpheus!
Orpheus: Your face is terrifying. So is your voice. What is your news?
Friend: Eurydice is dead.
(*Magnified crash of strings, as if all instruments smashed. Light effects—sudden darkening.*)
Narrator: Eurydice lies dead in the orchard, bitten by a snake.
Her soul has left her body. Her body is cold.
Her voice has been carried away to the land of the dead.
Orpheus: Eurydice!
(*He lies prostrate. His music—now erratic and discordant—struggles to tormented climax and again collapses as if all instruments smashed. Light effects.*)
Narrator: Orpheus mourns for a month and his music is silent.
The trees droop their boughs, they weep leaves.
The stones in the wall weep.
The river runs with sorrow under its willows.
The birds sit mourning in silence on the ridge of the house.
Orpheus lies silent and face downward.
His friends try to rouse him.
Friend: Orpheus, you are mourning too long. The dead are dead.
Remember the living. Let your own music heal your sorrow.
Play for us.
Narrator: The trees know better.
Trees: We shall never dance again. Eurydice is dead. Now we return to the ancient sadness of the forest.
Narrator: And the stones know better.
Stones: We are the stones, older than life. We have stood by many

graves. We know grief to the bottom. We danced for a while because Orpheus was happy. Eurydice is dead. Now we return to the ancient sadness of the hills.

Narrator: But still his friends try to rouse him.

Friends One, Two, and Three: Eurydice did not want you to grieve so long, Orpheus. Play your music. Deceive your grief. Defeat evil fortunes. The dead belong to the dead, the living to the living. Play for us.

Narrator: Have they succeeded?

At last! Orpheus reaches for the magic strings.

(*One note, repeated, gathering volume and impetus — insane*)

Friends One, Two, and Three: Horrible! Is this music? He has forgotten how to play. Grief has damaged his brain. This is not music.

Orpheus: I am going down to the underworld.

To find Eurydice.

Friends: Mad! He is mad! Orpheus has gone mad!

Orpheus: I am going to the bottom of the underworld.

I am going to bring Eurydice back.

Friend One: Nobody ever came back from the land of the dead.

Orpheus: I am going. And I shall come back.

With Eurydice.

Friends: Mad! He is mad! Orpheus has gone mad!

Nobody ever returns from the land of the dead.

(*Their voices fade. His crazy note strengthens, modulating into electronic, infernal accompaniments. Major light effects through what follows.*)

Narrator (*Speaking with greatly magnified voice over the music — not declaiming so much as a giant whisper*):

Where is the land of the dead? Is it everywhere? Or nowhere.

How deep is the grave?

What is the geography of death?

What are its frontiers?

Perhaps it is a spider's web. Perhaps it is a single grain of dirt.

A million million souls can sit in an atom.

Is that the land of the dead?

A billion billion ghosts in the prison of an atom

Waiting for eternity to pass.

(*ORPHEUS' music louder. Light effects.*)

Orpheus beats his guitar. He is no longer making music. He is making a road of sound. He is making a road through the sky. A road to Eurydice.

Orpheus: Eurydice! Eurydice! Eurydice!

Narrator: He flies on his guitar. His guitar is carrying him. It has lifted him off the earth. It lifts him over the treetops.

(*Music continuing, the monotonous note like a drum note insistent.*)

Friends: Orpheus, come back! Orpheus, come back!

Orpheus: Eurydice!

Narrator: It carries him into a cloud.

(*Light and sound effects through what follows, his music continuing throughout.*)

Through the thunder he flies. Through the lightning.

It carries him

Through the storm of cries,

The last cries of all who have died on earth,

The jealous, screaming laments

Of all who have died on earth and cannot come back.

(*Storm of cries.*)

Orpheus: Eurydice!

Narrator: He lays his road of sound across the heavens.

His guitar carries him.

Into the storm of blood,

The electrical storm of all the blood of all who have died on earth.

He is whirled into the summit of the storm.

Lightnings strike through him, he falls—

Orpheus: Eurydice!

Narrator: He falls into the mouth of the earth.

He falls through the throat of the earth, he recovers.

He rides his serpent of sound through the belly of the earth.

He drives his spear of sound through the bowels of the earth.

Mountains under the earth fall on him, he dodges.

He flies through walls of burning rock and ashes.

His guitar carries him.

(*Music continuing, monotonous and insane.*)

He hurls toward the centermost atom.

Orpheus: Eurydice!

Narrator: He smashes through the wall of the last atom.

He falls

He falls

At the feet of Pluto, king of the kingdom of the dead.

(*Silence. Appropriate light effects.*)

Pluto: So you have arrived. At first I thought it was a fly. Then I thought it was a meteorite. But now I see—it is a man. A living man, in the land of the dead. Stand. I am Pluto, king of the underworld. And you, I think, are Orpheus.

Narrator: Orpheus stands on the floor of the hall of judgment, like a mouse on the floor of a cathedral. Pluto's face, vast on his vast throne, is made of black iron, and it is the face of a spider. The face of Persephone, his wife and queen, vast on her vast throne, beside him, is made of white ivory, and it is the pointed, eyeless face of a maggot.

Pluto: Orpheus! I have heard of you. What is it, Orpheus, brings you alive to the land of the dead?

Orpheus: You took away my wife Eurydice.

Pluto: That is true.

Orpheus: What can I do to get her back?

Pluto: Get her back? (*Laughs—Plutonic laughter in hell.*)
Alas, your wife has gone into the vaults of the dead.
You cannot have her back.

Orpheus: Release her. You are a god. You can do as you like.

Pluto: Some things are not in my power, Orpheus. Here is my wife, for instance, Persephone. Perhaps you have heard about her. Six months she spends with me, here in the underworld. Six months she is up on earth, in the woods and meadows, with her mother. That is the arrangement. Up on the earth, she is a flower-face, she laughs and sings; everybody adores her. But now you see her. Here in the underworld she is quite different. She never makes a sound. Never speaks, never sings. And you see her face? It is the peaked face of a maggot. Yet it is not a maggot. It is the white beak of the first sprout of a flower. I have never seen it open. Here in the underworld it is closed—white, pointed, and closed—The face of a maggot.
Here is something I can't alter.
There is another thing, Orpheus. Here in the underworld, the accounting is very strict. A payment was due from you.

Orpheus: Payment.

Pluto: Nothing is free. Everything has to be paid for. For every profit in one thing—a payment in some other thing. For every life—a death. Even your music—of which we have heard so much—that had to be paid for. Your wife was payment for your music.
Hell is now satisfied.

Orpheus: You took my wife—

Pluto: To pay for your music.

Orpheus: But I had my music from birth. I was born with it.

Pluto: You had it on credit. You were living in debt. Now you have paid, and the music is yours.

Orpheus: Then take back my music. Give me my wife.

Pluto: Too late.

Orpheus: What good is music without my wife?
What can I do to make you give me my wife?

Pluto: Nothing can open hell.
(*ORPHEUS strikes a cord—no longer popular—solemn Handel, Bach, or earlier. Light effects.*)
Now what are you doing?
Your music is even more marvelous in hell
Than ever on earth. But it cannot help you.
(*Music.*)

Orpheus: Look at your wife, Pluto. Look at Persephone, your queen.
(*Music.*)

Pluto: Her face is opening.

Orpheus: A wife for a wife, Pluto. Shall I continue to play?

Pluto: Keep playing. Keep playing.
(*Music stops.*)
Keep playing. Why have you stopped?

Orpheus: It is in my power to release the flower
In your wife's face and awake her. Release my wife.

Pluto: Play.

Orpheus: A wife for a wife.

Pluto: Whatever you wish. Only play. You can have your wife.
(*Music.*)

Pluto: Beautiful as the day I plucked her off the earth!
(*Music stops.*)

Orpheus: You have your wife, Pluto.

Persephone: Keep your promise to Orpheus. Give him his wife.

Pluto: I cannot.

Orpheus: Cannot? A god cannot break his promise. A god's promise
is stronger than the god.

Pluto: I cannot. Your wife's body is crumbling to dust.

Persephone: Give him her soul.

Pluto: I can only give you her soul.

Orpheus: Let it be so. Let my wife's soul come with me.
(*Light effects. Dance and mime through what follows.*)

Pluto: You who have awakened the queen of hell,
Return to the world. Your wife's soul will be with you.
(*ORPHEUS' new music very soft*)
Narrator: Orpheus returns to the earth. It is not far.
It is only a step.
A step, a step, and a step.
A step—and he turns. He looks for his wife. The air is empty.
(*Music stops.*)
Orpheus: Eurydice?
Eurydice: I am here.
Orpheus: Eurydice, where are you? Eurydice?
Eurydice: Here at your side, Orpheus.
Narrator: He cannot see her. He cannot touch her. He can only hear
her. He listens.
Eurydice: Play for me, Orpheus.
(*ORPHEUS plays his new music.*)
Narrator: Orpheus' friends come running. They listen to his music. It
is no longer the same music.
Friend One: This won't make anyone dance.
Friend Two: This is queer music. He's gone to the dogs. This is dreary.
Friend Three: Play as you used to play, Orpheus. Make us dance.
(*Music continues*)
Narrator: The trees did not dance. But the trees listened.
The music was not the music of dancing
But of growing and withering,
Of the root in the earth and the leaf in the light,
The music of birth and of death.
And the stones did not dance. But the stones listened.
The music was not the music of happiness
But of everlasting, and the wearing away of the hills,
The music of the stillness of stones,
Of stones under frost, and stones under rain, and stones in the sun.
The music of the seabed drinking at the stones of the hills.
The music of the floating weight of the earth.
And the bears in their forest holes
Heard the music of bears in their forest holes,
The music of bones in the starlight,
The music of many a valley trodden by bears,
The music of bears listening on the earth for bears,
And the deer on the high hills heard the crying of wolves,

And the salmon in the deep pools heard the whisper of the snows,
And the traveler on the road
Heard the music of love coming and love going
And love lost forever,
the music of birth and of death.
The music of the earth, swaddled in heaven, kissed by its cloud and
watched by its ray.
And the ears that heard it were also of leaf and of stone.
The faces that listened were flesh of cliff and of river.
The hands that played it were fingers of snake and a tangle of flowers.

A CLOSER LOOK

1. What powers did the music of Orpheus have? Do you believe that music really could have such effects? Why, or why not?

2. Orpheus said, "The world is a gift. The brave take it with thanks and greet it with song." What did he mean by that? What did the voice mean by the words, "Every song has to be paid for."? What actually happened to Orpheus?

3. How did Orpheus use his music to influence Pluto, the king of the underworld? What did Pluto agree to do for Orpheus? How does the ending of the play differ from the ending of the original story of Orpheus and Eurydice?

V. Love Stories in Mythology

Throughout the ages, love has been an inspiration to poets, storytellers, and ordinary people. Love between man and a woman—a source of great joy and fulfillment—has always had, of course, the potential for tragedy as well. The myths contain many stories of love — love between gods and mortals, love between human lovers which, not infrequently, was influenced by the gods in some way.

Aphrodite (Venus), the goddess of love and beauty, symbolized love between men and women and, in nature, the force that reproduces life. The importance of Aphrodite's focus of concern was universally acknowledged, and altars to her could be found throughout the ancient world. The goddess of love not only inspired love in others, but was herself vulnerable to its forces. The story of Venus and Adonis showed that even the goddess of love was not beyond the pain of a tragic love affair.

Eros (Cupid), the son of Aphrodite, carried a bow and quiver of two types of arrows. One type inspired both gods and mortals to fall in love. The other produced exactly the opposite effect. Among the great love stories of mythology, that of Cupid and Psyche contains messages that are still worthy of consideration today.

From the myths have come the tales of many lovers, among them Apollo and Daphne, Endymion and Diana, Pygmalion and Galatea, and Pyramus and Thisbe. These stories demonstrate the timelessness and eternal nature of certain themes. The sad story of Pyramus and Thisbe, for example, parallels the tragedy told by Shakespeare centuries later in *Romeo and Juliet*. The musical *West Side Story* is a modern version of that tale.

From the Myths

VENUS AND ADONIS

● Even Venus, the goddess of love and beauty, was not immune to sorrow. Her love for Adonis was as intense and all consuming as a love could be, which made the untimely death of her lover especially tragic.

NE DAY, WHILE PLAYING WITH HER SON CUPID, Venus accidentally scratched herself with one of the boy's arrows. Before the wound healed, Venus happened to gaze upon Adonis, the extraordinarily handsome Prince of Phoenicia.

Venus was totally captivated by Adonis, and she adopted him and tutored him in the arts of love. Venus began to spend all her time away from Olympus, because the heavens were less important to her than her new-found love. For a time, Venus completely changed her way of life. No longer was she content to sit quietly contemplating[1] her beauty and cultivating her charms. She became more like the huntress Diana, and followed Adonis through fields and forests in pursuit of game.

Adonis was a fearless hunter, and Venus was concerned for his safety. She frequently urged him to confine his sport to those creatures who would cause him no harm, but he heeded her not. On one occasion, after warning Adonis to be careful, Venus flew off in her swan-drawn chariot and left her lover to hunt.

The dogs roused a wild boar from his lair, and Adonis threw his spear at the beast. The boar was wounded, but only slightly, and he managed to remove the spear with his jaws. The boar, by this time mad with pain, plunged his tusks into the side of Adonis. From her chariot, Venus heard the groans of her dying lover as his blood soaked the earth. She flew to his side, but it was too late.

Venus was inconsolable[2] in her grief, and Jupiter finally took pity on her and allowed Adonis to leave the underworld for six months each year. Those were the months of summer, when joy filled the land and the flowers grew. According to the poets, a red blossom grew from each spot of earth which had been touched by a drop of the blood of the dying Adonis. That is why Venus and Adonis are often credited with creation of the anemone, a brilliant crimson flower which still blankets grassy hillsides in what was once the ancient world.

[1]**contemplating:** observing thoughtfully
[2]**inconsolable:** not able to be comforted

Bion (translated by Andrew Lang)

THE LAMENT FOR ADONIS

● In ancient Greece, celebrations were held each spring in memory of Adonis. The following, part of an elegy intended to be sung at one of the spring celebrations to honor Adonis, was written by Bion, a Greek pastoral poet who lived around 250 B.C. The words and imagery vividly portray the anguish of Venus at the death of her beloved.

LOW ON THE HILLS IS LYING THE LOVELY ADONIS, and his thigh with the boar's tusk, his white thigh with the boar's tusk, is wounded; and sorrow on Cypris[1] he brings, as softly he breathes his life away.

His dark blood drips down his skin of snow; beneath his brows his eyes wax heavy and dim; and the rose flees from his lip, and thereon the very kiss is dying, the kiss that Cypris will never forego.

. . . She hath lost her lovely lord, with him she hath lost her sacred beauty. Fair was the form of Cypris while Adonis was living, but her beauty has died with Adonis! *Woe, woe for Cypris,* the mountains are all saying. And the oak trees answer, *Woe for Adonis!* And the rivers bewail the sorrows of Aphrodite,[2] and the wells are weeping for Adonis on the mountains. The flowers flush red for anguish, and Cytherea[3] through all the mountain-knees, through every dell, doth shrill the piteous dirge:

Woe, woe for Cytherea, he has perished, the lovely Adonis!

... When she saw, when she marked the unstanched wound of Adonis, when she saw the bright red blood about his languid[4] thigh, she cast her arms abroad, and moaned, "Abide with me, Adonis, hapless Adonis, abide!

... Awake, Adonis, for a little while, and kiss me yet again, the latest kiss!

... This kiss will I treasure, even as thyself, Adonis, since, ah, ill-fated, thou are fleeing me, thou art fleeing far, Adonis, and are faring to Acheron,[5] to that hateful king and cruel, while wretched I yet live, being a goddess, and may not follow thee. Persephone,[6] take thou my lover, my lord, for thyself art stronger than I, and all lovely things drift down to thee. But I am ill-fated, inconsolable is my anguish; and I lament mine Adonis, dead to me, and I have no rest for sorrow.

"Thou diest, oh, thrice-desired, and my desire hath flown away as a dream! Nay, widowed is Cytherea, and idle are the Loves along the halls! With thee has the girdle of my beauty perished. For why, ah, overbold, didst thou follow the chase, and being so fair, why wert thou thus overhardy to fight with beasts?"

So Cypris bewailed her, the Loves join the lament:

Woe, woe is Cytherea, he hath perished, the lovely Adonis!

A tear the Paphian[7] sheds for each blood-drop of Adonis, and tears and blood on the earth are turned to flowers. The blood brings forth the rose, the tears, the wind-flower.

Woe woe, for Adonis, he hath perished, the lovely Adonis!

... Cease, Cytherea, from thy lamentations,[8] today refrain from thy dirges.[9] Thou must again bewail him, again must weep for him another year.

[1] **Cypris:** Venus
[2] **Aphrodite:** Venus
[3] **Cytherea:** Venus
[4] **languid:** drooping from weakness
[5] **Acheron:** the river to Hades over which Charon ferried the dead
[6] **Persephone:** wife of Pluto, who spent six months each year in the underworld but returned to earth each spring
[7] **Paphian:** Venus
[8] **lamentations:** expressions of grief
[9] **dirges:** funeral songs

A CLOSER LOOK

1. What changes did Venus make in her life for Adonis? Do you think she should have done so? Why, or why not?

2. Why do you think Adonis enjoyed hunting dangerous animals? Do you think Venus should have made a greater effort to keep him safe? Why, or why not?

3. How did Venus handle her grief when Adonis was killed? Do you think her reaction was typical of how one might feel when a close loved one dies tragically? Why, or why not?

Aille X. West

CUPID AND PSYCHE

● Psyche's beauty rivaled that of Venus, the goddess of love and beauty. To punish Psyche, the jealous Venus told her son Cupid to cause the mortal maiden to fall in love with a monster. Instead, Cupid himself fell in love with Psyche. The story of Cupid and Psyche is a love story which shows the great damage jealousy and mistrust can cause.

ONCE THERE WAS A KING WHO HAD THREE daughters, each one lovelier than the next. The youngest, Psyche, was so extraordinarily beautiful that she rivaled Venus, the goddess of beauty. People in great numbers came from far and near to worship the lovely Psyche, and in doing so neglected the shrines of Venus herself.

Venus did not, of course, tolerate such a situation for long. To be upstaged by a mere mortal was more than any deity, especially the goddess of love and beauty, could endure. Venus called upon her son, Cupid, a lovely winged youth whose arrows brought certain love, to help her. "Use your powers," Venus directed her son, "to make Psyche fall in love with the most dreadful and vile creature in the world. That will punish her for her great beauty."

But all did not turn out as Venus had planned. When Cupid saw the lovely Psyche, her beauty so overcame him that he scratched himself with one of his arrows. Even Cupid himself had no defense against his own arrows, and he fell deeply in love with the maiden instead of causing her to love a monster. From that time on, no one sought

Psyche's hand in marriage, and the beautiful girl fell in love with no one. She led a life of sadness and solitude,[1] while her sisters married well.

Psyche's father could not understand why his most beautiful daughter remained unloved, and in desperation he consulted an oracle of Apollo. Cupid had already told Apollo the whole story, and Apollo had agreed to be of assistance. The oracle instructed Psyche's father to have the girl dressed in deep mourning and left on the peak of a rocky mountain. There, according to the oracle, Psyche's husband would find her and carry her off to whatever fate might be in store.

Psyche's family did as they were told, and left the girl alone on the rocky hilltop to meet her doom. There, as Psyche trembled in fearful anticipation of the unknown, she felt the gentle breath of Zephyr, the west wind, who lifted her up and carried her away. Zephyr, the kindliest of all the winds, set Psyche down in a flower-filled meadow near the banks of a stream. Nearby was a most magnificent mansion, which looked as if it had been built for a god.

Psyche wandered into the mansion and went from room to room. Everything was perfectly arranged, but the place seemed strangely deserted. Voices reassured Psyche that she was safe, and that everything she saw there was for her comfort. She bathed and dressed and feasted. Unseen singers and harpists entertained her with beautiful melodies and songs.

The voices kept Psyche company, and the girl was not lonely despite being unable to see anyone. When night came, her husband and lover was with her although she could not see him. She could tell from his voice and touch that he was not a monster.

As time went on, Psyche grew restless with the unusual arrangement which made it impossible for her to know the identity of her husband or to see him in the light of day. She longed to see her sisters, but her husband warned that they would cause her great harm. He finally permitted Psyche to see them anyway.

The sisters came to mourn at the spot where they had last seen Psyche alive, and the west wind brought them to Psyche. The joy at seeing each other once again quickly turned to conflict. The sisters, jealous of Psyche's palatial home and luxurious surroundings, were not satisfied by Psyche's answers to questions about her husband. "Why can't we meet him," they asked Psyche again and again. "Surely he must be some vile serpent or other horrible creature. If not, why would you not be eager to show him to us?"

Psyche did not know how to answer her persistent sisters, but the words of her husband kept ringing in her ears. "Do not be persuaded by anyone to attempt to look upon me," he had warned Psyche. "If you do so, you will lose me forever."

Psyche sent her sisters away, but she was unable to convince them that she was happy. Psyche's husband urged her not to see the sisters again, but she decided to meet with them one more time. Again, Cupid warned his wife, "Do not try to see my face. You must trust me, or you will lose me forever."

Psyche's sisters visited again, and this time they brought with them an evil plan. So jealous were they of Psyche that they spared no effort to convince the girl that her husband was a monster or worse. "Surely he would not shun the light of day unless he were a most vile and ugly creature," they told Psyche. And finally, Psyche began to believe them·

"What should I do?" Psyche asked her sisters. "How can I find out to what kind of creature I am married?"

The sisters eagerly replied. "Tonight, when you are certain your husband is sleeping soundly, take a knife and a lamp," they said. "Hold the lamp so that you see his face and, before he wakes, plunge the knife into the monster who has taken you from us. We will wait outside, and carry you home."

Psyche reluctantly prepared to do the bidding of her sisters. Her heart was torn. Should she trust the husband she believed to be loving and wonderful even though she had never seen him? Should she trust her sisters? Would it really matter if she lit the lamp long enough to take just one little look? Would he ever know?

Night came. Psyche, still torn by doubt, decided to see for herself what sort of creature her husband might be. She waited until he was sleeping soundly. Then she lit the lamp and held it in her left hand. In her right hand she clutched a sharp knife. As she held the lamp high over the bed, there before her eyes was the most handsome and lovely man she had ever seen. It was the god of love himself!

Psyche drew back in horror and guilt at what she had done. She, who had the most wonderful husband in the world, had been faithless and untrusting. Her remorse[2] was so great that she considered, for a fleeting moment, plunging the knife into her own breast. And, had her hand been steady, she might have done so, but the sight of her love filled her with the desire to live with him forever.

Drawing closer to the bed, Psyche held the lamp high in order to see her husband's beautiful face more clearly. As she did so, a drop of hot oil fell upon Cupid's shoulder and awakened him. While Psyche stood in shocked disbelief, Cupid arose and fled. "Love cannot remain," he said, "where there is no trust."

Psyche ran after her husband, but he had vanished into the darkness. "I must search for him," Psyche said to herself. "I will spend the rest of my life searching for him. I'll think of some way to show him my love."

Part 2

Psyche began what seemed like an endless journey to find her husband. She had no idea where to go or what to do. She knew only that she was destined to wander until she was successful in her quest, even if that took a lifetime or more.

Cupid, most distressed, went home to his mother. He begged Venus to aid him, soothe his wound, and comfort his bereaved heart. Venus, however, became enraged when Cupid told her the story. Not only had her son failed to follow the order to make Psyche fall in love with a vile creature, but he had fallen in love with the girl himself! Venus offered her son no solace.[3] Instead, the angry goddess vowed to punish Psyche still further.

Psyche wandered from place to place in great despair. She beseeched various gods for assistance in her plight, but none would risk angering Venus. Finally, in desperation, Psyche went to the home of Venus herself. There Psyche was received with anger and scorn. "Why should I help you?" Venus asked the unhappy girl. "My son lies suffering greatly from the torture of the burning oil you spilled on him. Why do you think he would have anything further to do with you?"

Then Venus gave Psyche a task to complete. The goddess took several handfuls of the smallest seeds—wheat, poppy, millet, and barley—and, after mixing them thoroughly, tossed them in a heap. "Sort these before the night comes," Venus told Psyche, "Things will not go well for you if you fail."

Psyche looked at the seemingly impossible task in front of her. Her eyes were too clouded by tears to see the tiny seeds. Her fingers were too tremulous[4] even to begin the task. Then, suddenly, the tiny ants took pity on her and helped. Thousands of them scurried from every corner of the field and placed the seeds each with its own kind. By nightfall the job was done. Psyche's success did not please Venus, however, but only enraged the goddess more.

The next morning, Venus ordered Psyche to accomplish an even more difficult task. She sent Psyche to fetch golden wool from the fierce sheep near the river. Psyche was so terrified and unhappy that she contemplated throwing herself into the river and ending it all. But as she leaned over the water, the voice of a reed told her not to despair. "Wait until evening," the gentle reed advised. "When the sheep come out of the bushes to rest, you will be able to collect bits of fleece from the briars."

Psyche waited and, just as the reed had promised, the bushes were filled with clumps of fleece that had caught on the thorns. Psyche gathered the golden wool and took it to Venus. Again the goddess was furious. "Someone helped you," she said. "The next task won't be so easy."

Next Venus sent Psyche to fill a flask with water from the source of the River Styx. Psyche went in the appointed direction only to find a dark waterfall crashing against the slimy rocks. Only a winged creature could accomplish the task Venus had assigned. But, just as Psyche was losing all hope, an eagle arrived, took the flask in his beak, and returned it full of murky water. Once again, Venus took Psyche's success as a spur to demand fulfillment of an even more difficult task.

Venus told Psyche to go to the underworld and ask Proserpine for some beauty. Venus gave the girl a box, and told her to return with it filled with Proserpine's beauty. Once again, just as Psyche thought she would never solve the problem, the needed help came. A mysterious guide told her how to enter Hades through a hole in the earth. She was advised to pay the ferryman, Charon, a penny to carry her safely across the river of death. A biscuit tossed to Cerberus, the three-headed dog, would ensure her admission to the underworld in order to complete her task.

Proserpine was willing to do the bidding of Venus, and it wasn't long before Psyche was on her way back with the box containing some of Proserpine's beauty. Psyche was unable, however, to resist the temptation to open the box even though she had been warned of dire consequences if she did so. Her curiosity, along with a desire to acquire a bit of beauty in case she should meet Cupid, caused her to lift the lid. The box seemed empty, and Psyche fell into a deep sleep from which no mortal could emerge without divine help.

At this point, Cupid could stand the situation no longer. Convinced of Psyche's love for him despite the girl's foolishness, Cupid relented and flew to her aid. He awakened Psyche and then sought help from

Jupiter. Jupiter listened to Cupid's story and decided that the lovers had suffered enough. He gathered the gods together and announced the heavenly marriage of Cupid and Psyche. He permitted Psyche to sip from a cup of ambrosia, thus making the girl immortal. Even Venus could not object to having Psyche as a daughter-in-law now that the girl was a goddess instead of an ordinary person.

Cupid and Psyche, or Love and Soul as they are sometimes called, having found each other and having survived trials, were destined to remain together always. And, according to some poets, the two soon produced a daughter whom they named Pleasure.

[1] **solitude:** state of being alone or isolated
[2] **remorse:** deep regret for having done something
[3] **solace:** comfort
[4] **tremulous:** quivering from fear

A CLOSER LOOK

1. What benefits did Psyche enjoy in her unusual marriage? What disadvantages did she face? How do you think you would have coped with such an arrangement if you had been in Psyche's place? Explain and support your answers.

2. Why did Psyche's sisters refuse to accept Psyche's story that she was happily married? Why do you think Psyche finally gave in to her sisters? Do you think Psyche deserved the punishment she got? Why, or why not?

3. "Love cannot remain where there is no trust." Do you agree? Why, or why not? Do you think Cupid and Psyche deserved a happy ending for their story? Explain and give reasons for your answer.

From the Myths

APOLLO AND DAPHNE

● Apollo, a handsome and magnificent god, was sought after by many, but not by all. The nymph Daphne, for example, resisted Apollo's advances with every means available to her. Much to Apollo's eternal despair, Daphne resorted to extreme means to avoid the sun god's love.

DAPHNE WAS A YOUNG, EXTREMELY BEAUTIFUL wood nymph who disliked men and even the thought of men. She had no interest in marriage and, like Diana the huntress, preferred to roam on her own through the wild. Daphne's father, the river-god Peneus, was most dismayed because Daphne rejected every suitor who came her way. Peneus feared that he would never know the joy of grandchildren.

Apollo, the sun god, fell victim both to Daphne's beauty and to her disdain.[1] This all came about because of Cupid, who played a malicious trick on Apollo, in return for something Apollo had done to him. Apollo, who believed himself to have no rival as an archer, saw young Cupid one day playing with a bow and arrows. "Leave such weapons to those with experience," Apollo told Cupid. "They are not toys for a mere boy."

Cupid became quietly enraged at Apollo's arrogance, and vowed to show the older god just how experienced he was and how devastatingly powerful were his arrows. Cupid waited until Apollo was near the

nymph Daphne. Then he shot two arrows—the leaden one to repel love and the golden one to incite love. The leaden one hit Daphne, and caused her to reject Apollo just as she had rejected scores of human suitors. The golden arrow hit Apollo, and caused him to fall deeply in love with Daphne.

Apollo pursued his love through the forest. Daphne ran as fast as she could to escape. Apollo, his heart flaming with love, called after the fleeing nymph. "Be not afraid, for I am the god of song and the lyre. My heart has been pierced by an arrow more powerful than any of my own. Even the god of medicine and healing, which I also am, has no cure for Cupid's arrows. I love you."

Daphne continued to run. Apollo, being both swift and a god, drew nearer. Daphne, growing desperate, feared that she would be unable to elude her pursuer much longer. When she reached the riverbank, she begged Peneus to help her. "Help me, Peneus! Please, my father, change my form so that I might escape from him who seeks me."

Hardly had the words fallen from Daphne's lips, when she began to stiffen and change her appearance. Soon the young maiden had become a laurel tree. Apollo threw his arms around the tree, embraced it, and lavished kisses on its bark. "You cannot be my wife," he told the laurel, "but you will always be my favorite tree. Of your branches I'll make a crown, and the laurel wreath will become a symbol of honor. And, as a token of my eternal love, your leaves will remain forever green, and not decay."

[1]**disdain:** scorn; a feeling of contempt for something or someone deemed unworthy

A CLOSER LOOK

1. Why did Apollo tell Cupid to leave the bow and arrow to someone with more experience? Do you think he should have done so? Why, or why not?

2. Why do you think Daphne refused Apollo's advances? Do you think she was right to do so? Why, or why not?

3. Why did the laurel become a symbol of honor? What special quality did Apollo bestow upon the laurel leaves? Why did he do so?

From the Myths

ENDYMION AND DIANA

● Endymion was an attractive shepherd who caught the attention of Diana, the goddess of the moon. Diana, who once had vowed never to fall in love with a man, fell deeply in love with Endymion, and a way was found to ensure that their love would be eternal.

ENDYMION, A SHEPHERD, WAS DESCRIBED BY THE poets as a most beautiful youth. His attractiveness was so appealing that Diana, the huntress and moon goddess who had pledged never to become involved with a man, fell in love with Endymion and broke her vow.

That night, as the poets told it, was calm and clear. Diana gazed down upon the beautiful Endymion as he slept. Her usually cold and unyielding heart was touched by the youth's beauty which surpassed that of any other she had seen. She came down to him and kissed and caressed him as he slept. Diana found Endymion to be irresistible, and returned to him night after night.

Diana's secret love for Endymion could not long be concealed from the others on Mount Olympus. Her frequent absence from her heavenly duties aroused considerable suspicion, and no one would believe she had been out hunting on every occasion she was missing from Olympus. Her pale face and weariness caused many to wonder what had transpired the night before.

Endymion is said to have achieved an eternity of sleep along with eternal youth which enables him to enjoy the dreams brought by the mistress of the moon who, whenever possible, slips away from her nocturnal[1] obligations to visit him.

The precise details of how Endymion entered into a state of perpetual sleep vary from one poet to another. Some say that the youth, upon being discovered as the one who had accepted the moon's advances, was punished by Jupiter and forced to choose between death and eternal sleep. Others say that Endymion, having greatly enjoyed the caresses of the moon, begged Jupiter for perpetual sleep so that he might have the pleasure of sharing his dreams with the moon throughout eternity.

[1]**nocturnal:** of the night

● The following poem by Edith Hamilton captures the story of Endymion and Diana in a very few words. Selene was the name given to an ancient goddess of the moon who later became associated with Diana.

Edith Hamilton

ENDYMION THE SHEPHERD

Endymion, the shepherd,
As his flock he guarded,
She, the Moon, Selene,
Saw him, loved him, sought him,
Coming down from heaven
To the glade on Latmus,
Kissed him, lay beside him.
Blessed is his fortune.
Evermore he slumbers,
Tossing not nor turning.
Endymion the shepherd.

A CLOSER LOOK

1. What scene in nature did the ancient Greeks attempt to explain by the story of Endymion and Diana?

2. What characteristics of Endymion led Diana to fall in love with him?

3. Do you think Endymion was free to choose whether or not to fall in love with Diana? Why, or why not?

Ovid (Retold by Annie Mueser)

PYRAMUS AND THISBE

● Long and long ago, the berries of the mulberry tree were said to be white as snow. How these berries achieved their deep red hue has been told by the Latin poet Ovid, in *Pyramus and Thisbe*, a tale of tragic young love. In this story, you may also find roots of later works such as *Romeo and Juliet, West Side Story*, and *The Fantasticks.*

ONCE UPON A TIME, IN THE WALLED CITY OF Babylon during the reign of Queen Semiramis, lived two of the finest and loveliest young people one could ever know. Pyramus, a handsome youth, and Thisbe, a beautiful maiden, were the closest of neighbors—so close, in fact, that they grew up separated only by the common wall between their houses. And as time went on, they fell in love.

Sadly for Pyramus and Thisbe, their parents would not let them marry. But the flames of true love are not easily extinguished, and the desires of the two became increasingly intense as their parents forbade the union. The hated wall which separated the lovers also brought them comfort, for unknown to anyone the builders had left a small defect there. Pyramus and Thisbe found this tiny opening and made of it a passageway for words of love. But the kisses pressed on opposite sides of the wall had no way to reach the lips for which they were intended, and the young lovers grew desperate.

Each night, as the time for them to part drew near, Pyramus and Thisbe whispered fervent[1] farewells through the chink in the wall. And each morning, after dawn had swallowed up the stars and the sun's early

rays had dried the dewy grass, they again took their places, one on each side of the wall, to exchange words of love. Finally the lovers could stand their plight no longer, and they agreed to meet in secret, face to face.

Pyramus and Thisbe decided to wait until the cover of darkness and then meet outside the city walls at the Tomb of Ninus, a well-known place. They arranged to meet under the tall tree there, a mulberry laden[2] with snow-white berries, near a cool bubbling spring. So pleased were they with their plan, it seemed to them as if the day would never end. But at last the waves consumed the setting sun, and night filled the sky.

Thisbe, her face concealed in the folds of her cloak, was the first to reach the appointed spot. There, while she waited in the moonlight for her beloved, she saw a lioness. The fierce beast, mouth dripping with the blood of a newly killed calf, approached the spring to slake her thirst. The terrified Thisbe, leaving her cloak in the dust, fled to the safety of a nearby cave.

The lioness, after drinking from the spring, tore Thisbe's cloak before retreating to her den. A few moments later, Pyramus arrived and saw the bloody remnants[3] of Thisbe's garments on the ground next to the footprints of the savage lioness. Certain that Thisbe had been devoured by the beast, and filled with remorse that he had not arrived in time to save her, Pyramus went to the planned meeting place under the mulberry tree. Clutching what was left of Thisbe's cloak, Pyramus plunged his sword into his side. His blood sprayed the snow-white berries, and turned them to crimson.

In the meantime, Thisbe cowered[4] in the cave, fearing to come out lest the lioness attack. But, unwilling to fail her lover, the young woman gathered her courage and ventured forth. She searched for the mulberry tree, but could find none with white berries. But then, beneath a tree with dark red berries she saw a slight movement. There on the ground she found Pyramus, bleeding and dying. "It is I, your dearest Thisbe," she cried as she cradled his head in her arms. He opened his eyes for a last look, and then died.

The grief-stricken Thisbe saw what was left of her own cloak next to the sword fallen from her beloved's hand and realized immediately what had happened. "Your love for me and your own hand has caused your death," she cried to the lifeless Pyramus. "We once believed that only death would have the power to part us. I defy even death to have that power now." And she took the sword still wet with the blood and plunged it into her own heart.

Both the gods and the lovers' parents were moved by the tragedy and Thisbe's final prayers. The ashes of the two were placed in the same urn. And, from that time on, the ripe fruit of the mulberry remained a deep red color in everlasting memory of the tragic lovers.

[1] **fervent:** having great warmth and intensity of spirit or feeling
[2] **laden:** loaded down; burdened
[3] **remnants:** remains
[4] **cowered:** crouched in fear

A CLOSER LOOK

1. Why did Pyramus and Thisbe have to communicate through a chink in the wall? Do you think they might have grown tired of each other if they had been able to associate freely? Why, or why not?

2. What did Pyramus see that led him to conclude Thisbe had died? How did his conclusion turn out to be incorrect? What were the consequences of that mistake?

3. What were some of the reasons the parents of Pyramus and Thisbe might have tried to prevent their union? What could any of the people involved have done to prevent the tragic outcome of the story? Explain and give reasons for your response.

From the Myths

PYGMALION AND GALATEA

• Pygmalion was an artist, a sculptor, who hated women. Despite his feelings for the female sex, he labored long and lovingly over a statue of a woman. When his work was done, his life seemed exceedingly incomplete. Pygmalion, like so many others, turned to Venus, the goddess of love for aid.

P YGMALION, A YOUNG AND TALENTED SCULPTOR from Cyprus, was said to hate women. He had absolutely no intention of ever marrying, and he devoted all his energies to his work. Despite his claim to hate women, however, Pygmalion's major project involved the creation of a life size statue of a woman.

Pygmalion spared no effort to ensure that his creation was as perfect an image of a female form as possible. He worked long and lovingly over every detail. The creature he made was exquisite[1] in every way. Pygmalion was so engrossed[2] in his work that he didn't realize what was happening to him. Each stroke of the chisel rendered his creative spirit more closely intertwined with the object of art before him. Each touch of the hand to polish and smooth the statue's surface became a caress.

Finally, when his work on the statue was done, Pygmalion stepped back and looked at what he had wrought.[3] Confident that his extraordinary efforts had resulted in perfection, he was filled with pride in his accomplishment. But instead of happiness, his heart was filled with longing. Oddly and sadly, this man who vowed never to fall in love with a woman had done so. But the object of his affections was not a live, flesh and blood creature who could love him back. The object of his ardor[4] was the piece of art he had just made.

Pygmalion talked to the statue, and hugged and kissed her as if she were real. But the statue's inability to return the attentions was extremely frustrating for Pygmalion. He became totally obsessed with his creation, and desperate for her love.

Finally Pygmalion sought the help of Venus, whose feast day was especially honored in Cyprus, the island which the goddess first visited after she arose from the foam of the sea. On the special day of Venus in Cyprus, Pygmalion went to the altar of the love goddess. Venus was fascinated by the unusual situation presented by the young artist who had fallen in love with his art.

Afraid to admit what he really desired, Pygmalion asked only for a maiden somewhat like the statue. Venus, however, being wise in all affairs of the heart, knew exactly what Pygmalion was seeking. She knew that a similar maiden would not suffice.

When Pygmalion returned home, he greeted the statue with kisses and caresses as he usually did. But this time something was different. The cold sculpted surface of the marble began to grow warm to his touch. Slowly the statue began to move and breathe. No longer a statue but a real woman, the young artist's creation stepped off the pedestal and into his waiting arms.

Pygmalion named the maiden Galatea, and it is said that Venus herself graced their marriage with her presence.

[1] **exquisite:** having special beauty and appeal
[2] **engrossed:** occupied completely
[3] **wrought:** produced
[4] **ardor:** passion, great warmth of feeling

A CLOSER LOOK

1. Why do you think Pygmalion, despite his apparent dislike of women, put so much effort into creating a statue of one?

2. How did Pygmalion's own life and personality change as a result of his work?

3. Who are the people who have most influenced the sort of person you are today? What kind of influence do you have on others? How does this differ from what Pygmalion was able to do with his art?

● It was the festival of Venus, and the celebration at the shrine of the goddess was about to begin on the island of Cyprus. The altar of the goddess was surrounded by clouds of incense, as Pygmalion approached with his words of pleading. As you read the following lines by poet Andrew Lang, try to put yourself in Pygmalion's shoes.

Andrew Lang

THE NEW PYGMALION

O Aphrodite, kind and fair,
    That what thou wilt canst give,
Oh, listen to a sculptor's prayer,
    And bid mine image live!
For me the ivory and gold
    That clothe her cedar frame
Are beautiful, indeed, but cold;
    Ah, touch them with thy flame!
Oh, bid her move those lips of rose,
    Bid float that golden hair,
And let her choose me, as I chose,
    This fairest of the fair!
And then an altar in thy court
    I'll offer, decked with gold;
And there thy servants shall resort
    Thy doves be bought and sold!

VI. Heroic Tales...
Tasks of Hercules

I n the myths of the ancient Greeks and Romans, gods and humans often mingled freely and produced children with a god for one parent and a mortal for another. Some of these special children turned out to possess unusual strength and courage, and many fascinating tales are told of their heroism.

Perseus, the son of Zeus (Jupiter) and Danae, the daughter of King Acrisius, killed Medusa, a snake-haired monster who turned to stone anyone who looked at her face. Another Greek hero was Theseus, who challenged King Minos of Crete, battled the Minotaur, and escaped from the Labyrinth.

Atalanta, who was banished by her father because she was not a boy, lived in the wild and became a strong and clever huntress. She and Meleager, her lover, led the hunt for the destructive Calydonian boar.

The quest for the Golden Fleece was another adventure for which those who would be heroes gathered. Jason and his forty-nine men undertook a perilous voyage and eventually captured the prize they sought.

Perhaps the greatest of the Greek heroes was Heracles, who is better known by his Latin name, Hercules. Hercules, who had superhuman strength and courage, became famous for his performance of twelve seemingly impossible tasks—the Twelve Labors of Hercules. These tasks were (1) to kill the Nemean Lion; (2) to kill the nine-headed hydra; (3) to bring back alive the stag with golden horns; (4) to capture a great boar; (5) to clean the Augean stables in a single day; (6) to conquer a plague of birds; (7) to take a fire-eating bull from King Minos; (8) to master the man-eating horses of King Diomedes; (9) to bring back the girdle of Hippolyta; Queen of the Amazons; (10) to fetch the cattle of the monster, Geryon; (11) to obtain the golden apples of Hesperides; (12) to bring Cerberus, the three-headed dog, up from Hades. Hercules became so famous for accomplishing these difficult tasks, that even today something requiring extreme effort is referred to as a "Herculean task."

From the Myths

PERSEUS, THE AVENGER

● King Acrisius wanted a son, but had only his daughter Danae. He consulted the oracle at Delphi, who predicted that the King would have no sons, but that Danae would have a son who would, sooner or later, kill Acrisius. Danae's son, Perseus, became a hero by killing Medusa, a dreadful monster whose face, surrounded by writhing snakes, could turn to stone anyone who set eyes on it.

KING ACRISIUS OF ARGOS HAD ONE CHILD, A daughter named Danae. The King, who desperately wanted a male heir, consulted the oracle at Delphi to ask if he would ever have a son. He was told that he wouldn't have a son and, even worse, that his daughter would eventually bear a son who would kill him.

An obvious solution to the King's dilemma would have been to kill Danae so that she could never marry and have children. Acrisius did not do so, however, because he feared the wrath of the gods. Instead, he locked Danae in a tower where she could not associate with anyone. The plan failed, however, when Zeus assumed the form of a golden cloud of light and entered the tower to visit Danae. Danae later gave birth to a son, whom she named Perseus. The name Perseus means "the avenger."

It was difficult to keep a growing boy secret for very long, and King Acrisius soon discovered his grandchild. The King devised a way to get rid of both Danae and Perseus without actually killing them. He had a

wooden boatlike chest constructed to hold them, and he set the two afloat on the sea. He then left the rest to the forces of nature.

The chest neither sank nor broke apart in the waves, and finally it floated to shore. A kindly fisherman named Dictys came to the rescue of mother and child, opened the chest, and offered the two a home. They lived in peace on the island for a number of years. But then trouble came again. The island was ruled by Polydectes, brother of the fisherman who had rescued Perseus and Danae. Polydectes had designs on Danae, who was still a very attractive woman, but he had to figure out a way to get rid of Perseus.

Polydectes had told Perseus about the Gorgons, dreadful and deadly monsters who lived on an island. He told the boy that what he wanted most in the world was the head of one of the Gorgons. Then Polydectes, who said he was about to be married, held a party to which he invited friends and acquaintances, including Perseus. The only one without a gift for Polydectes was Perseus who, in his embarrassment, promised he would return with the head of Medusa, the most terrible of all the Gorgons, as a gift. Fortunately for the impetuous[1] Perseus, who had made the promise without truly understanding the possible consequences, the gods offered protection.

Both Hermes and Athena took it upon themselves to assist Perseus in his quest. Killing Medusa would not be easy, because the scaly neck of the Gorgon could bend the sword of any ordinary mortal. Even more hazardous to Perseus was the fact that anyone who looked at Medusa would immediately turn to stone. What would have been an impossible task, however, became possible with the help of the gods. Hermes

107

supplied a special unbreakable sword with which to attack Medusa. Athena provided a polished shield which could be used as a mirror so Perseus could kill the Gorgan without looking directly at her.

Hermes directed Perseus to find the nymphs of the North, who would give him three additional items he needed. To find the nymphs, it was necessary to ask directions of the three gray women, old hags who shared but one eye among them. Perseus grabbed the eye, and refused to give it back until the directions had been given to him. Accompanied by Hermes, Perseus finally reached the North where he received the three needed gifts: winged sandals, a magic pouch which assumed the correct size for whatever was put in it, and a cap which made the wearer invisible.

Perseus was well equipped to do battle with Medusa. Looking into the mirrorlike shield, he was able to see the reflection of the monster's grotesque[2] head with writhing[3] snakes for hair. But because he didn't look at the monster directly, he was not turned to stone. The sword, guided by the hand of Athena, did the job as promised without bending or breaking. The pouch closed itself around the severed head of the Gorgon with ease, so that Perseus could carry it away.

Carrying the head of Medusa, Perseus returned to the island where he had left his mother. He got there just in time to prevent Polydectes from forcing Danae into marriage. Perseus walked into the gathering of wedding guests with firm strides. After warning his mother to shut her eyes, he withdrew the head of Medusa from the pouch. "Here is what I promised you," he told Polydectes. "Look upon your gift." Polydectes and his friends were immediately turned to stone as they gazed at the snake-infested head of Medusa.

Perseus and Danae decided to make an effort to find Acrisius and seek reconciliation.[4] They were less than successful. At an athletic contest, Perseus threw a discus which accidently went astray. The spectator who received the fatal blow was Acrisius, the former King of Argos. Thus the prophecy of the oracle was fulfilled. Perseus did kill his grandfather even though he did not intend to do so.

[1] **impetuous:** rash; quick to act without thought
[2] **grotesque:** fantastically ugly
[3] **writhing:** twisting
[4] **reconciliation:** achievement of harmony and agreement

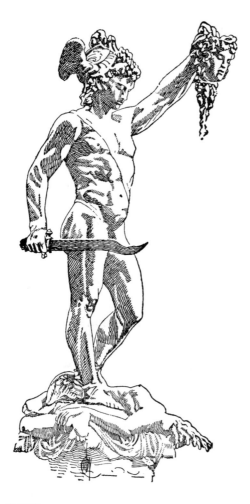

A CLOSER LOOK

1. *Why did King Acrisius lock his daughter in the tower? In what way did his plan fail? Why did he send Danae and Perseus to sea in a chest?*

2. *How did Perseus manage to kill Medusa? From whom did he obtain help? What might have happened if he had not taken the steps he did?*

3. *When the prophecy of the oracle was fulfilled, do you think King Acrisius got what he deserved? Why, or why not? If Perseus or Danae had been able to determine how their story would end, what do you think would have happened? Why?*

From the Myths

THESEUS

● The great hero of Athens was Theseus, the son of the Athenian King, Aegeus. Theseus became known not only for his heroic deeds, but for his compassion and intellect as well. Perhaps the most famous of his accomplishments took place in Crete, where he entered the Labyrinth in pursuit of the deadly Minotaur.

THESEUS, SON OF THE ATHENIAN KING AEGEUS, spent his early days at the home of his mother in southern Greece. Aegeus had returned to Athens before the child was born. He had left behind a sword and a pair of shoes, which he had placed in a hollow covered by an extremely heavy rock. "If the child is a boy," Aegeus had told his wife, "when he is strong enough to roll away the stone, he may take the things he finds there and come to Athens where I will acknowledge him as my son."

When Theseus grew strong enough to move the great stone, he removed the sword and shoes and prepared to seek his father. Although a ship was available to him, Theseus preferred to travel by the much more hazardous overland route. He enjoyed taking risks, and had as a goal to become a great hero as rapidly as possible.

Theseus believed—quite correctly—that facing the dangers of the road to Athens would help him achieve heroic stature more quickly than would a peaceful sea voyage. Along the way he managed to kill the terrible bandits who plagued the route. He dispatched[1] them all, and left not a one to bother future tavelers.

The way in which Theseus finished off each bandit reflected the manner in which that person had dealt with his own victims. Sciron, for example, who had forced his victims to bathe his feet before he kicked them into the sea, was hurled off a cliff into the deep waters below. Theseus arranged for Procrustes to be tortured on the same iron bed Procrustes had used for those he killed. Theseus had a very simple code of justice. Each person received what he had previously done unto others.

When Theseus finally arrived in Athens, he was acclaimed as a great hero. He made himself known to his father by drawing his sword, which Aegeus immediately recognized as the one he had placed beneath the stone many years earlier.

The Minotaur

The accomplishment for which Theseus received the most acclaim was his successful battle against the Minotaur. The Minotaur was a monster, half bull and half human. He ate human sacrifices. This dreadful creature lived in the Labyrinth, a maze from which there was virtually no escape for those unfortunate enough to be forced to enter it.

The story of the Minotaur is a somewhat complicated one. Years earlier, a terrible thing had happened to the City of Athens. Androgeus, the only son of King Minos of Crete, had been visiting King Aegeus. While there, the young man, who had joined in a hunt for a wild bull, was killed by the bull instead of the other way around. King Minos, enraged by the loss of his only heir, invaded and captured Athens, and threatened to destroy the city and level it to the ground unless his conditions were met. These conditions included the requirement that every nine years Athens send a tribute[2] of seven youths and seven maidens.

The Minoteur lived in the Labyrinth, a tortuous[3] maze that had been designed by Daedalus, a clever inventor and architect. Once inside the Labyrinth, a person faced twisting paths seemingly without end or exit. Lurking around the next bend or about to emerge from the shadows was the Minotaur, a monster whose great pleasure was to devour the humans placed there in tribute.

When Theseus came to Athens and presented himself to King Aegeus, it was just about time for the next group of young people to be

sent off for consumption by the Minotaur. Theseus volunteered to go. He was lauded by the Athenians for his generosity and nobility. What Theseus did not tell the people, however, was that he intended to kill the Minotaur rather than be a meal for a monster.

Theseus shared his plan with his father, and King Aegeus was worried. Theseus told the King to look at the sail of the returning ship. If the sail was black, as it always was when it carried the cargo of young people to their death in the labyrinth, that would mean that Theseus had died. If the sail had been changed to white, that would mean that Theseus had succeeded in his mission and was still alive.

When Theseus and the other youthful victims reached Crete, they were forced to parade through the streets on the way to the Labyrinth. Among the spectators was Ariadne, the daughter of King Minos. She saw Theseus and fell in love with him on the spot. Ariadne went to Daedalus in search of information about how to escape from the maze. She then told Theseus she would tell him how to get out of the Labyrinth if he would marry her and take her back to Athens. Theseus, given a choice between certain doom in the Labyrinth and marriage to a lovely maiden, agreed to marry Ariadne.

Ariadne gave Theseus a ball of thread which he was to unwind as he roamed the maze. To retrace his steps and exit he would simply have to rewind the thread. Theseus did as he was instructed, and only dropped the ball of thread long enough to kill the Minotaur with his bare hands. He then wound up the thread and found his way out of the Labyrinth.

Although Theseus was long remembered by the Athenians for killing the Minotaur and ending the practice of sending young men and women to Crete to be sacrificed, his story did not end in perfect triumph. Although Ariadne began the voyage back to Athens, she never reached the destination. According to one story, Ariadne fell asleep and Theseus simply sailed off without her. A kindlier tale, however, related how Theseus had left a seasick Ariadne on shore to regain her strength. A storm separated them and by the time Theseus returned, the young woman had died. When he finally sailed into the harbor of Athens, Theseus forgot to lower the black sail and hoist the white one. His father, who had long waited for a sign that Theseus had been successful, saw the black sail and thought that his son had been killed. In his grief, King Aegeus threw himself off a rocky cliff into the sea which, from that time on, has been known as the Aegean Sea. A sadder but wiser Theseus became King of Athens where he created a government in which the people enjoyed liberty, justice, and self rule.

[1] **dispatched:** killed
[2] **tribute:** an enforced contribution or payment
[3] **tortuous:** twisting and turning

A CLOSER LOOK

1. Why did Theseus choose to travel to Athens by the overland route rather than by sea? What does his decision reveal about his character?

2. What was the code of justice Theseus followed in dealing with the bandits he found on his way to Athens? Do you agree with his choice of punishments?

3. How did Theseus defeat the Minotaur? What happened when Theseus returned to Athens after killing the Minotaur?

FROM THE MYTHS

ATALANTA

● Were there two heroines named Atalanta, or just one? Although two men, Iasus and Schoenius, have each been called the father of a heroine named Atalanta, the stories are similar. Perhaps there was only one Atalanta, but several versions of her story. Here is one of them.

WHEN ATALANTA WAS BORN, HER FATHER WAS extremely vexed that the child was not a boy. Believing that it would be a waste of time to raise a girl, he left his daughter on a mountainside to freeze or starve to death. A she-bear found the infant, however, and provided warmth and nourishment. Atalanta grew strong, bold, and lively. Kindly hunters took her in, and she became a superb huntress who feared nothing. When two centaurs[1], for example, pursued her in the forest, she calmly stood her ground and felled each with a single arrow.

Atalanta's most notable hunting achievement came in the famous hunt of the Calydonian boar. The boar, which ravaged[2] the land and caused extraordinary destruction, had been sent by Artemis to Calydon as punishment for the failure of the King to honor the goddess at the time of the harvest.

In desperation, King Oeneus of Calydon called upon brave men of Greece to come to his aid. Some of the finest young heroes of that land

114

gathered to help fight the vicious Calydonian boar. Atalanta, confident of her skill, joined the group in quest of the boar. Meleager, the son of Oeneus and leader of the hunt, fell instantly in love with Atalanta.

Some of the heroes who thought of hunting as an activity for men only were unhappy and resentful that a female should dare to invade their sport. Meleager insisted that Atalanta was welcome, however, and fortunately his wishes prevailed. The hunters surrounded the boar, but the creature charged and killed two men at once. A a third hunter was dispatched[3] by an errant javelin hurled by one of his own colleagues. Despite the commotion, Atalanta was able to wound the boar with an arrow. Meleager, finishing what Atalanta had started, stabbed the beast in the heart.

Meleager awarded the skin of the boar to Atalanta, and this gesture angered some of the men. Among those who protested giving the boarskin to a girl were Meleager's two uncles, brothers of his mother, Althea. The two ordered Meleager to take the prize away from Atalanta and to apologize for having insulted them. Meleager countered their demand by killing them both.

Meleager's hasty move to avenge the insult to Atalanta caused his own death in a strange and indirect way. Years earlier, when Meleager was just a week old, the Fates had appeared to Althea and had thrown a log of wood into the fire. They told Althea that her newborn son would live until the wood turned to ash. Althea quickly removed what was left of the charred bit of wood from the fire. She cooled it and hid it away so the burning would never be complete.

Raging because her son had killed her brothers, Althea took the wood from its hiding place and tossed it into a flame. Althea immediately had second thoughts about her impulsive[4] action, but it was too late. As the flame consumed the wood, Meleager fell to the ground and died in Atalanta's arms. Atalanta believed she would never love again.

After Meleager's death, Atalanta coped with her grief by living an active and adventurous life. She expressed an interest in sailing with the Argonauts, although there is no evidence that she actually did so. After the Argonauts returned, Atalanta took part in an athletic contest and in the wrestling match defeated Peleus, a young man who later became the father of Achilles, a hero of the Trojan War.

Atalanta finally learned the identity of her parents, and she went to live with them. She forgave her father for abandoning her years earlier because he wanted a boy child. He, in turn, admired Atalanta's many accomplishments and at last accepted his daughter. Atalanta's parents hoped that their daughter would marry, but the young woman refused to let any man replace the memory of Meleager in her heart. She spurned[5] all suitors.

Under pressure from her parents and many suitors, Atalanta devised a plan to deal with those who sought her hand. She agreed to marry any man who defeated her in a foot race. Atalanta, who was extremely fleet of foot, knew that no such man existed. In race after race, hopeful young men were beaten.

Finally one day a young man named Hippomenes challenged Atalanta to a race. Hippomenes, who had already fallen deeply in love with Atalanta, consulted Aphrodite, the goddess of love. Aphrodite gave Hippomenes three golden apples and instructions for their use. When the race started, Atalanta quickly drew ahead. Hippomenes, however, tossed a golden apple in her path and she paused to pick it up. When Atalanta again took the lead, Hippomenes tossed the second apple. Again Atalanta stopped for a moment to retrieve the golden fruit, and again she sped ahead. As they approached the finish line, it appeared that Atalanta would surely win. Hippomenes, however, tossed the last of the three apples far to the side. Atalanta, with a strong push from the goddess of love, left the path of the race and went after the apple. As she bent to pick up the last of the golden apples, Hippomenes crossed the finish line and claimed Atalanta as his bride.

Atalanta's days of living in the wild and enjoying the hunt had finally come to an end. But she found Hippomenes to be a most compatible husband and, had the two not offended the gods, they might have lived happily ever after. Unfortunately for them both, however, something they did or did not do turned out to be an affront[6] to Aphrodite. In punishment, Atalanta and Hippomenes were turned into wild beasts, and had to live out their days as a lion and lioness.

[1] **centaurs:** mythical creatures who were half man and half horse
[2] **ravaged:** devastated; ruined
[3] **dispatched:** killed; finished off
[4] **impulsive:** without thought
[5] **spurned:** rejected
[6] **affront:** insult

A CLOSER LOOK

1. Why did Atalanta grow up in the wild? How did her early environment affect her development? How did Atalanta and her father finally mend their relationship? Why do you think they were able to do so.

2. What were the reasons Atalanta and Meleager were well suited for each other? What happened to Meleager? How did his death affect Atalanta?

3. How did Hippomenes finally win Atalanta? What became of the couple?

Rex Warner

JASON

● Jason was one of the best known heroes and adventurers of ancient Greece. More than fifty others joined him on the voyage in quest of the golden fleece. Between Jason and success stood numerous incredible obstacles. A combination of heroism, strength, favor of the gods, love, and perhaps just plain luck supported Jason's efforts.

JASON, WHO WON THE GOLDEN FLEECE, WAS THE first man to build a ship. He was also the first to lead an expedition of Greeks against the East. His father, Aeson, had been driven from the throne of Iolcos by Pelias, his half-brother, and had been forced to live in a poor house, with all his wealth and all his honors taken away from him. At this time Jason was a small boy, not strong enough to defend himself, and Aeson feared for his son's safety. He therefore put the the boy in the care of the wise centaur, Chiron. In music, medicine and archery Chiron was the most famous of teachers, and in all these subjects Jason quickly became himself an expert.

As he grew to manhood, Chiron advised him to consult the oracle as to what he should do with his life. "Return to Iolcos," the oracle replied to his question, "and demand from Pelias the kingdom that rightfully belongs to your father."

Jason therefore said good-bye to Chiron and came down from the mountans to the plain. On his way to Iolcos he had to cross a river which at this time of year was swollen with rain water from the melting snow on the mountain peaks. When Jason reached this river he saw waiting on the bank an old woman who asked him to help her across. When he was in midstream, he was surprised to find that, in spite of his strength, the old woman seemed to weigh him down, as though she were heavier than the size of her would suggest. As he struggled, one of his sandals slipped from his foot and was swept away by the stream.

When he reached the other side, he set the old woman down and turned to look at her, but she had disappeared, and he knew that he had been visited by one of the gods. It was in fact Juno, the wife of Jupiter, who had been neglected by King Pelias, and who, ever afterwards, helped Jason and supported him.

After addressing a prayer to the goddess, Jason went on his way to the city. King Pelias himself looked at Jason with interest and also with fear. This was because an oracle had told him that one day he would have his kingdom taken from him by a man wearing only one sandal. He immediately summoned Jason to him and asked who he was and what was his business in Iolcos. Jason boldy and in front of all the people said that he had come to claim the kingdom that had been wrongfullly taken from his father. As he spoke the people admired the young man's courage and plainly showed that they were on his side. Pelias said to Jason: "If you are indeed worthy of what you claim, you must prove your worth. What I wish you to do is this—to avenge the death of our relative Phrixus and to bring back to Greece the Golden Fleece."

Jason knew the story of Phrixus. He also knew that Phrixus had been related to him since his own grandfather had been the brother of Athamas, who had had by his first wife, Nephele, two children who were called Phrixus and Helle. Later Athamas had married Cadmus's daughter Ino, and Ino, jealous of her step-children, had plotted to kill them. But the boy and girl were saved by a ram with golden fleece, which was given to them by Mercury. On this animal's back they escaped from Thebes and even crossed the sea. The girl Helle grew tired on the way and fell into the sea which is still called the Hellespont after her; but Phrixus arrived safely at the court of King Æetes who ruled over the land of Colchis at the far extremity of the Black Sea. Instead of treating Phrixus hospitably, Æetes had murdered him in order to have the golden fleece of the ram.

Jason, though he knew that King Pelias hoped that this adventure would cost him his life, determined nevertheless to undertake it. He let it be known that he intended to lead an expedition to the east, and from

all over Greece young men and heroes came to Iolcos. In the end fifty-three men and one woman sailed on the *Argo*, a miraculous ship built by the craftsman Argos. It had in its prow a beam cut in the oak woods of Dodona. This beam was capable of speaking in a human voice and pronouncing oracles.

The ship was launched to the music of the famous singer, Orpheus, who went himself on the expedition. Tiphys was the steersman. Other heroes who sailed with Jason were Hercules, the son of Jupiter, Lynceus, whose eyesight was so keen that he could easily see quite small objects at a distance of nine miles, Aesculapius, the great doctor, Calais and Zetes, the winged sons of the North Wind, Meleager and Calydon and many others. The one woman who sailed was Atalanta, famous as a huntress and as a runner. All these heroes are known as the Argonauts, since they were sailors in the *Argo*.

THE VOYAGE OF THE ARGONAUTS

Very many adventures took place on their way through the sea to Colchis. First they landed at the island of Lemnos and were surprised to find not a single man in the place. It was governed entirely by women under their queen, Hypsipile.

Queen Hypsipile fell deeply in love with Jason, and Jason promised her that, after he had won the Golden Fleece he would return to Lemnos and make her his wife. As we shall see, he did not keep his promise. But so hospitably were the Argonauts received at Lemnos that they stayed there for a whole year.

After a year's stay at Lemnos, the *Argo* put to sea again. Among the Argonauts were the two brothers Castor and Pollux, sons of Zeus. Pollux was particularly skillful as a boxer, and this skill was of great service to his companions when they came to the kingdom of King Amycus, the son of Neptune, whose custom it was to challenge all strangers to a boxing match. Those who lost the match (and so powerful was the king that he had never been defeated) were compelled to serve him as slaves or else were put to death. The Argonauts and the followers of King Amycus stood in a circle to watch the fight, and soon it was evident that, though perhaps Amycus was the stronger of the two, Pollux had the greater skill. He lightly avoided the king's enormous blows and, leaping inside his guard, raised great red marks on his ribs and stomach as he struck with the heavy gloves. He maneuvered carefully, so that the king would have the sun in his eyes, and now, changing his tactics, he began to strike at the face. Finally, growing desperate, Amycus seized hold of Pollux's right arm with his left and, while he was so held, smashed a blow at him which, if it had landed, would certainly have killed him. But Pollux slipped his head aside and, striking out from the shoulder, struck Amycus such a blow on the temple that the king fell to the ground in a heap.

Next the Argonauts came to the court of the blind King Phineus, who was gifted with prophetic powers. The king indeed attempted to entertain them hospitably, but, no sooner were they seated at the tables and the food was set out than there swooped down from the air three terrible monsters called the harpies or "Snatchers." These creatures had women's faces and the bodies and wings of large vultures. They

121

pounced upon the tables, flapping their huge wings, fouling everything with the mess they made, knocking over the goblets of wine and filling their greedy and disgusting mouths with whatever they could take up. So Phineus, in the midst of all his riches, had not been able for years to eat one meal undisturbed. This was a punishment which had been sent him by the gods, because he had used his prophetic powers to reveal secret things. Now, however, the day of his deliverance had come, for among the Argonauts were the two winged sons of the North Wind, Calais and Zetes.

Now the young children of the North Wind drew their swords and sprang into the air, since they were winged. The Harpies fled away. Iris, the goddess of the rainbow, appeared and said: "Cease your pursuit, Calais and Zetes! It is not for you to destroy the Harpies. But Jupiter promises that never more will they come to afflict Phineus. Now return, and ask the king to tell you of the dangers that lie in front of you and Jason and your friends."

The brothers obeyed her and flew back to the palace of Phineus where, for the first time in years, the king was able to enjoy an unmolested meal.

When the meal was over, Jason turned to the king and said: "We have been glad to help you to escape from your persecution. Now we ask you to help us. Tell us, if you will be so kind, what other dangers we are to expect before we reach the land of Colchis."

"Your greatest dangers," Phineus said, "will be in the land of Colchis itself, and of these I may not speak. What I can tell you is that, before you enter the Black Sea, at its very gateway, you will have to pass between two blue rocks that are called the Symplegades, or Clashers. Those rocks guard the straits. At one moment they move apart from each other; at the next they dash together with such violence that anything, whether it be a bird or a ship, that is caught between them is immediately crushed and broken to pieces. When you reach those rocks, what I advise you to do is to take a pigeon and let it go free. If the pigeon succeeds in flying unscathed between the rocks, that will be a sign to you that the gods are not unfriendly. Watch the rocks carefully, and, when they move apart, row with all your might.

Jason and the Argonauts listened with astonishment, and fear. This was a danger which they had never imagined. Nevertheless they again set to sea. The winds favored them, and it was not long before, on the distant horizon, they saw what appeared to be sheets of water spouting into the air. As they drew nearer they were aware of a noise like thunder, and soon they could see clearly the two blue and craggy rocks that intermittently leaped apart and sprang clashing together, sending up clouds of water as they met, and deafening the ears with the roar of their impact. Beyond them was the surface of another sea, and there was no way to reach it except between these clashing mountains.

Jason took his stand in the stern so that from there he could urge on the rowers. First, he prayed to all the gods and especially to Juno, and liberated a white dove. The next moment, as the spray subsided, the Argonauts raised a shout of joy. The dove had flown through in safety and was already winging its way over an unknown sea.

Again the rocks clashed together. Then, as they parted, Jason shouted out the word of command. The rowers bent over their oars and the ship's timbers seemed to shiver as she leaped through the rough and foaming water. With a tremendous splintering crash the two rocks came together again; but the *Argo* was through.

THE GOLDEN FLEECE

The Argonauts finally reached the court of King Æetes, and there, surrounded by his brave companions, Jason asked that the Golden Fleece be returned to the kinsman of Phrixus.

The king, seeing so many and such brave champions in front of him, was at a loss for a reply. Finally he spoke: "I admit that your claim is just, but I can grant it only on these conditions. Tomorrow at sunrise, you must yoke my bulls to the plow. You must plow a field and then sow there the teeth of a dragon. If you are successful in these tests, you may take the Golden Fleece, but you must take it yourself and singlehanded from the serpent who is its guardian. These are my terms. Tell me if you will accept them."

The gods made Jason bold. "They have helped me so far," he thought. "Will they not help me to the end?" He looked resolutely at the king. "I accept your conditions," he said. "But if I do my part you must do yours."

The king smiled as he agreed. Only he and his daughter Medea, who was sitting at his side, knew that the tasks he had proposed were beyond the strength of any mortal man. As for Medea, her mind was carried this way and that way as she looked now at the brave and beautiful stranger whom she was seeing for the first time. "What I feel," she said to herself, "is either love or something like what people call love. I cannot bear the thought of this stranger perishing and I want to save him. Yet, if I do so, I shall be betraying my father and my native land. What will become of me? I cannot bear to lose him. If I can help him, he must take me with him to Greece. I should have to leave my father and my home, but I should be the wife of a great hero and I should be renowned myself for my magic arts and for saving all the best of the Greeks."

So she thought to herself, and in the evening she met Jason in a wood. Jason took hold of her right hand, and, in a low voice, begged her to help him, promising that, if she did so, he would take her away with him and marry her. She burst into tears and said: "I know that what I am doing is wrong, but I shall do it. Only swear that you will keep your promise."

Jason then swore by Hecate, by the all-seeing Sun and by all the gods that he would be true. Medea gave him the magic herbs and told him how he must use them in the perils of the next day.

When dawn came, crowds flocked to the sacred field of Mars and stood all round it on the heights above. King Æetes, in a purple robe and carrying an ivory scepter, sat on his throne with Medea at his side and his people all round him. Suddenly into the fields came the bulls. They had hooves and horns of brass, and through their iron-hard nostrils they blew out fire and smoke. The grass shriveled and caught on fire as they breathed on it, and the noise of their breathing was like the noise of a roaring furnace. Jason went to meet them, and, as he approached, they turned their terrible faces upon him, pawed the ground with their brazen hooves and shook their metal horns, filling the whole air with fiery bellowings. The Argonauts, as they watched, stood stiff and silent in terror; but Jason went up to the bulls, and, so great was the power of the magic herbs that he had received, did not feel the burning of their fiery breath. With one hand he boldly stroked their swinging dewlaps[1]; then he put the yoke on their necks and forced them to draw the heavy plow and furrow up the field that had never felt iron before.

Next Jason took the dragon's teeth from a brazen helmet and began to sow them in the plowed field. The teeth, steeped as they were in powerful magic, grew soft in the earth and began to swell up into new forms. Just as a child grows gradually inside the mother's body, and does not come out into the world until it is a fully shaped human creature, so these seeds grew under ground and did not emerge to the surface of the earth till they had taken on the shapes of fully-grown men, complete with weapons which they clashed together. When the Greeks saw this army of warriors preparing to hurl their sharp spears at Jason's head, again their faces fell and again their hearts failed them. But Jason took up a great rock and hurled it into the middle of the earth-born army.

This had the effect of turning all their rage and anger upon themselves. Man fought man until the whole lot of armed men had perished by each other's hands.

Then the Argonauts thronged round Jason, embracing him and cheering and congratulating him on his victory. Medea, too, would have liked to embrace him, but was afraid of what people might say. All she could do was to look at him with silent joy and thank the gods who had given her such powerful spells.

All that remained now was to face the terrible dragon that guarded the Golden Fleece. It was a creature with a great crest on its head, a three-forked tongue and curving hooked teeth. It was coiled around the stem of the tree where, through the thick dark leaves, glowed a gleam of gold, showing where the fleece was. Jason sprinkled on the dragon some juices from herbs of forgetfulness which Medea had given him. Then three times he recited a spell strong enough to make stormy seas calm or to force swollen overflowing rivers back into their beds. Gradually and for the first time sleep came over the dragon's eyes. Jason threw the heavy fleece across his shoulder and hurried to his ship with the Greeks and with Medea. They were sailing down the river almost before Æetes had realized what had happened. They reached open sea safely, and sailed joyfully back to Iolcos.

[1] **dewlaps:** the loose fold of skin hanging from the throat of cattle and certain other animals is called a dewlap

A CLOSER LOOK

1. What business did Jason have with King Pelias? How did Jason get the support of the people of that Kingdom? What did Pelias ask Jason to do to prove his worthiness? Why did he do so? Why did Jason agree?

2. What was unusual about the ship **Argo** *and its crew? What hazards did Jason and his followers face on their voyage? How did they deal with each one?*

3. What did Jason have to accomplish to gain possession of the Golden Fleece? How did he manage to succeed?

From the Myths

THE LABORS OF HERCULES

● Hercules, the greatest of Greek heroes, was the strongest and most confident man on earth. He believed he could never be defeated by any mortal, and the events of his life ultimately proved him right. As penance for acts committed during an insane rage, Hercules sentenced himself to do the bidding of Eurystheus, King of Mycenae. Eurystheus assigned twelve tasks, which have become known as the "Labors of Hercules."

HERCULES WAS THE STRONGEST MAN ON EARTH AND certainly the most confident. Unlike Theseus, whose heroism was a product of intellect as well as strength and daring, Hercules depended far more on his physical strength than on brains. His extraordinary strength coupled with easily aroused emotions and a hot temper sometimes got him into serious difficulties. Hercules had the additional problem of being a son of Zeus, a condition which ensured that a jealous Hera would cause troubles from time to time.

The best possible education was made available to Hercules, but he did not graciously cooperate for subjects he disliked. Music was one such subject, and during a music lesson Hercules became so angry that he dealt his teacher a fatal blow to the head with a lute. On a number of occasions throughout his life, Hercules who sometimes seemed not to know his own strength, took actions which had unanticipated consequences. He was always full of remorse, however, when his emotions got out of hand and caused harm.

The most tragic of the misdeeds of Hercules occurred when Hera caused him to become mad. In his insanity, Hercules killed his beloved wife and three sons. When the madness left him, he realized what he had done. He knew that extraordinary penance would be required. He turned himself over to King Eurystheus of Mycenae, and sought to be assigned suitable tasks of penance. The twelve tasks which were set before Hercules were virtually impossible, but in each instance Hercules gave his best effort. These tasks have become known as the "Labors of Hercules," and their tales have been told many times over.

 LABOR #1

The first of the assignments given to Hercules was to kill the Nemean lion. Killing a lion would ordinarily require no special effort, but the great lion of Nemea was not an ordinary lion. The Nemean lion was invulnerable to weapons of any kind, so that arrows, clubs, or spears were destined to have no effect. Hercules solved the problem, however, by strangling the beast with his bare hands.

 LABOR #2

The second task Hercules faced was to kill the nine-headed hydra, a dreadful creature that lived in a swamp at Lerna. This task was especially difficult because one of the heads of the hydra was immortal, and for each of the remaining eight, two grew when one was chopped off. Finally Hercules, with the help of his nephew Iolaus, used a flaming branch to sear the stump of each neck so no new heads could grow. Hercules finished the job by burying the immortal head under an enormous boulder.

 LABOR #3

The third labor was to capture the stag with the golden horns. This animal was sacred to Artemis, and the task assigned to Hercules involved bringing the animal back alive. It would have been far easier to hunt and kill the creature, but Hercules knew that would never do. Instead, Hercules managed to wound the animal just enough to slow him down without killing him. Then Hercules picked up the stag and carried him to King Eurystheus. The successful completion of this task took more than a year.

 LABOR #4

The fourth task involved the capture of a massive and fierce boar which roamed wild on Mount Erymanthus and ravaged[1] all in his path. Like the stag, the boar was to be brought to King Eurystheus alive. The strategy Hercules employed to accomplish the fourth task was to chase the beast from one place to another until the boar finally grew tired. Then Hercules drove the exhausted animal into the deep snow where he trapped it in a huge net.

 LABOR #5

The fifth labor assigned to Hercules was to clean the Augean stables in a single day. Cleaning stables would not normally be an impossible task, but the Augean stables were not typical stables. Augeas, King of Elis, kept a herd of some three thousand oxen in these stables, and the stalls had not been cleaned in at least thirty years. Hercules managed to do the job by diverting two rivers—the Alpheus and the Peneus—through the stables long enough to wash out all the filth. As soon as the task had been completed, Hercules permitted the rivers to return to their beds.

 LABOR #6

The sixth task set before Hercules was to conquer and destroy the Stymphalian birds. These birds, which were present in great number, plagued the people of Stymphalus with sharp cruel beaks and sharpened talons. These warlike birds were a favorite of Ares, and were extremely difficult to hunt. Athena helped Hercules flush the birds out of their coverts,[2] and then Hercules shot each one.

 LABOR #7

The seventh labor of Hercules involved taking the fire-eating bull from King Minos of Crete. This bull was a magnificent but savage creature given by Poseidon to Minos. Hercules used his own brute strength to master the animal and load him aboard a ship to bring to King Eurystheus. Hercules carried the bull from the boat on his shoulders to present him to Eurystheus.

 LABOR #8

The eighth labor assigned to Hercules was to master the man-eating mares of King Diomedes of Thrace. These swift steeds subsisted on human flesh, and capture of them was no easy task. Hercules accomplished the job by first killing Diomedes and feeding him to the beasts. Then Hercules was able to round up the animals and drive them to King Eurystheus.

 LABOR #9

The ninth labor of Hercules was to bring back the girdle of Hippolyta, Queen of the Amazons. The Amazons were a nation ruled by warlike women, who brought up only their female children. Some boys were sent to neighboring nations; others were killed. At first it appeared as if Hercules would be able to accomplish the ninth labor with ease. Hyppolyta was hospitable and gracious, and she agreed that he could take the girdle. Hera, however, ensured that nothing would ever be too easy for Hercules. She stirred up the Amazon women and led them to believe that Hercules intended to capture their Queen. When the Amazons stormed the ship, Hercules acted in impulse and haste. He killed Hyppolyta instantly because he believed her to be behind the attack, and then he sailed for home.

 LABOR #10

The tenth task Hercules had to complete was to fetch the cattle of the monster Geryon and bring these animals to King Eurystheus. Geryon was a monster with three bodies who lived on an island called Erythea (the red) which was so named because it lay to the west, the direction of the setting sun. On his way, Hercules was said to have split a mountain in two, leaving one half on each side of what is now the Strait of Gibraltar. Hercules killed those guarding the cattle, including a giant and a fierce two-headed dog. He then brought the cattle safely to King Eurystheus.

 LABOR #11

The eleventh labor was an especially tricky one for Hercules. The task involved bringing back the golden apples of the Hesperides. In order to accomplish this, Hercules first had to find out where the apples were. He asked Atlas, father of the Hesperides, to help him. Atlas, who held the heavens on his shoulders, agreed to get the apples if Hercules would take over holding the sky while he did so. Atlas handed the sky to Hercules and obtained the apples. He was so delighted to be free of his heavy burden that he decided never to take it back.

Fortunately for Hercules, Atlas was not especially clever. Hercules asked Atlas to relieve him for a moment to place a pad to cushion his shoulders. When Atlas took back the sky so Hercules could get comfortable, Hercules simply picked up the apples and left.

 LABOR #12

For the final task of the twelve, Hercules had to bring Cerberus, the three-headed dog, up from Hades into the upper world. This was not something that could have been accomplished without the help of the gods, and both Mercury and Minerva accompanied Hercules to Hades. Pluto gave Hercules permission to bring Cerberus to the upper world as long as no weapons were used. Hercules managed to subdue the animal and carry him in his bare hands to King Eurystheus, who wisely directed Hercules to return Cerberus to Hades immediately. So ended the last of the Labors of Hercules.

[1] **ravaged:** devastated; ruined
[2] **coverts:** thickets providing shelter for game birds or animals

A CLOSER LOOK

1. What sort of person was Hercules? How did certain of his personal characteristics cause difficulties for him? Which of his traits were beneficial?

2. Why did Hercules undertake the tasks which have become known as the Labors of Hercules? Do you think these labors were suitable punishment for him? Why, or why not?

3. What was the nature of each of the twelve labors? What strategy did Hercules employ to complete each task? What conclusions can you draw about Hercules from his performance on these tasks?

● Even after completion of the twelve labors, the life of Hercules was far from dull. He married Dejanira, sister of Meleager of the Calydonian hunt. Dejanira became jealous of Hercules and poisoned him with the charmed blood of the Centaur Nessus. When Hercules approached his funeral pyre ready to die, Zeus ensured that only the mortal portions of the hero's flesh would be consumed by the flames. Hercules was then permitted to join the gods on Mount Olympus. The lines that follow tell of the ultimate triumph of Hercules.

J. C. F. von Schiller (translated by S. G. Bulfinch)

THE DEATH OF HERCULES

Deep degraded to a coward's slave,
Endless contests bore Alcides[1] brave,
Through the thorny path of suffering led;
Slew the Hydra, crushed the lion's might,
Threw himself, to bring his friend to light,
Living, in the skiff that bears the dead.
All the torments, every toil of earth,
Juno's hatred on him could impose,
Well he bore them, from his fated birth
To life's grandly mournful close.

Till the god, the earthly part forsaken,
From the man in flames asunder[2] taken,
Drank the heavenly ether's purer breath.
Joyous in the new unwonted lightness,
Soared he upwards to celestial[3] brightness,
Earth's dark heavy burden lost in death.
High Olympus gives harmonious greeting
To the hall where reigns his sire adored;
Youth's bright goddess, with a blush at meeting,
Gives the nectar to her lord.

[1] **Alcides:** Hercules
[2] **asunder:** apart
[3] **celestial:** heavenly

VII. The Trojan War, The Odyssey, Adventures of Aeneas

The Trojan War has been described as one which began with an apple and ended with a horse. The apple, a golden one inscribed "For the Fairest," was tossed among guests at the wedding of King Peleus and the sea nymph Thetis. The provocative apple and resulting dispute among three goddesses, each of whom claimed to be the fairest, set into motion a complicated chain of events which lasted many years.

Paris was given the task of choosing which goddess was the fairest. To reward him for his choice, the favored goddess granted him Helen, the fairest woman in the world. Paris took his prize off to Troy, and Helen's husband, King Menelaus, called on all of Greece to fight for Helen's return. A decade later that war, which was complicated by the involvement of various gods on each side, finally ended. Odysseus (Ulysses) used a wooden horse full of soldiers to enter and defeat Troy.

The Fall of Troy did not end the hardships for Odysseus and his men, for the triumphant Greeks had insulted the gods. As a result, their voyage home was filled with punishing perils. The Ciconians killed many of the Greeks as they slept on the beach. Eating lotus flowers put the men to sleep. Polyphemus, the one-eyed monster, threatened to consume them all.

Before his ten-year voyage ended, Odysseus faced many additional hazards. His men were turned into swine by Circe. They had to avoid the song of the Sirens and the monsters of Scylla and Charybdis. All but Odysseus died in a storm as punishment for eating the cattle of the Sun. Odysseus spent the next seven years on an island with the nymph Calypso, but finally found his way home. He then had to face the many suitors who had sought the hand of his wife Penelope in his absence.

Aeneas was another hero of the Trojan War whose years after the war were filled with hardships and adventures. After Aeneas escaped from Troy, his voyage to Italy involved some of the same hazards that Odysseus met. Again various gods took sides in the unfolding events. Eventually Aeneas triumphed and founded the Roman state.

From the Myths

THE TROJAN WAR

● The story of the Trojan War has been told in one of the world's greatest poems, the *Iliad*, by the blind Greek poet Homer. The war began with an apple, ended with a horse, and contained numerous complications involving gods and humans on both sides. The incident with the apple, often referred to as "the judgment of Paris," was a decision which set into motion a chain of events lasting a decade.

ERIS, THE GODDESS OF DISCORD, WAS (FOR OBVIOUS reasons) not the most popular party guest on Mount Olympus or anywhere else. Those who wished a festive occasion unmarred by troublemaking took pains not to invite Eris. The goddess was the only divinity not invited to the marriage feast of King Peleus and the sea nymph Thetis. Furious at the insult, Eris tossed a golden apple inscribed "For the Fairest" into the banquet hall.

All the goddesses at the wedding wanted the apple, but the choice quickly narrowed down to Aphrodite, Hera, and Athena. Zeus was clever enough not to risk making a choice, and he referred the goddesses to Paris, a mortal prince who was living as a shepherd near Troy. Paris was the son of King Priam of Troy, who had been warned that his son would someday be the ruin of Troy, and therefore sent him away.

When the three goddesses arrived, they did not ask Paris to choose the fairest. They each offered him something and asked him to state his preference. Even so, the choice was difficult. Hera promised him he would lead the Trojans to victory over Greece. Athena promised him wisdom with which he could develop winning tactics. Aphrodite, the goddess of love, vowed to grant him the most beautiful woman in preference to power, and he handed the apple to Aphrodite.

Hera and Athena were absolutely furious at this turn of events, and they vowed to retaliate in some way. Aphrodite kept her promise to Paris by recommending that he seek out Helen, a Spartan queen who, according to the goddess, was the mortal who most resembled herself. Helen was, as Aphrodite was quick to point out, extremely worthy of being called the most lovely on earth. Helen's mother was Leda, who had been loved by Zeus himself in the form of a swan.

There was a major complication, however, to any arrangement which would grant Helen to Paris in reward for the judgement of Paris which had declared Aphrodite to be the fairest. That complication was Helen's husband, King Menelaus of Sparta. Paris, aided by Aphrodite, cast aside his life as a shepherd and resumed his position as Prince of Troy. He then went to Sparta as if on a diplomatic mission, and within a day of meeting Helen at a state banquet had her aboard his ship sailing back to Troy.

Before her marriage to Menelaus, Helen had been sought by kings and princes from throughout the ancient Greek world. Her father had been reluctant to give her hand in marriage because he feared that the many unchosen suitors would band together and destroy his kingdom. To avoid this possibility, all the suitors took an oath to let Helen make her choice. They vowed not to attack the victorious suitor, but instead to defend in time of need. When Paris stole Helen away, all who had taken the oath to defend her were obliged to come to the aid of King Menelaus. It wasn't long before a thousand ships were assembled and made ready to sail to Troy to recapture Helen.

The Greeks were in for a long battle. They realized that Troy would not fall quickly, but would have to be taken by siege[1]. Troy was a securely walled city, and the Greeks camped outside and tried to fight their way in. Ten years later, in a war that had been complicated by interventions of various gods and goddesses on both sides, the Greeks were still trying to enter the fortified city. The defense of Troy was carried out by the fifty sons of Priam, who fought fiercely and well to defend their homeland. Even when Hector, their greatest warrior, was killed by the Greek hero Achilles, the Trojans were not defeated.

Finally Ulysses, one of the greatest and cleverest of the Greek heroes, devised a scheme to defeat Troy. Suddenly, the Greeks gave the impression that they had given up the battle. Their camps outside the walls were removed, and their ships sailed out of the harbor as if starting toward home. The Trojans, having managed to kill Achilles by an arrow to his heel, the only spot in which he was vulnerable[2], believed that the Greeks had really surrendered.

The removal of the encampments and the departure of the ships was just a ruse[3], however, and the Greeks had not really abandoned the battle at all. They had left behind them on the beach a mammoth wooden horse which the Trojans thought to be an offering to Poseidon, god of the sea. Unknown to the Trojans, the horse was hollow, and inside hid Ulysses and a number of his very best men.

What happened next was just what Ulysses, the master tactician[4] who had devised the horse plan, had anticipated. Overcome by joy at the siege finally being ended, the Trojans began to celebrate what they perceived to be their long awaited victory. They began by wheeling the great horse into the city. But their celebration was short lived. That night, as all Troy slept and dreamed of victory, Ulysses and his men came out of the underbelly of the huge wooden horse. They murdered the sentries[5] and opened the gates of Troy. In swarmed the rest of the Greeks who by this time had sailed under cover of darkness and reestablished the camps on the beaches at the city's edge.

The Greeks, led by Ulysses, took the Trojans completely by surprise. Those who were not slaughtered were made captive slaves. The city soon fell in flames and ruins. And so what had begun a decade earlier with an apple, ended with a horse.

[1] **siege:** long drawn out process of surrounding and attacking a fortified place in an effort to cut off supplies and weaken resistance
[2] **vulnerable:** capable of being harmed
[3] **ruse:** trick
[4] **tactician:** someone who is clever in making strategic plans
[5] **sentries:** guards

A CLOSER LOOK

1. *What was meant by the "judgement of Paris"? Why did Paris make the choice he did? Do you think he could have made a better choice? Why, or why not?*

2. *The Trojan War has been described as beginning with an apple and ending with a horse. Why? What did you learn about Ulysses from his role in the way the war ended?*

3. *Why did Paris at one time live as a shepherd rather than as the Prince of Troy he really was? What eventually occurred to prove that King Priam had been correct?*

From the Myths

THE VOYAGE OF ODYSSEUS

● After Troy fell, Odysseus and his men set sail for home. Because they had angered the gods greatly, the voyage became fraught with perils. The resulting ten-year journey of Odysseus (or, Ulysses, as he was also known) was described in Homer's famous poem the *Odyssey*.

AFTER THE DESTRUCTION OF TROY, THE GREEK warriors made haste to sail for home. In preparation for their journey, however, they plundered the ruins of the burning city for anything valuable they might carry away. They even committed the unspeakable acts of violating temples and places sacred to the gods. In return, the offended gods ensured that the voyage would not be easy and that few would complete it successfully.

The Greeks' long odyssey[1] began uneventfully, and the weary warriors were well on their way before a turbulent[2] storm drove them far off course. When they finally reached shore, they were in a strange but lovely land called Lotus, where they consumed quantities of a delicious and sweet-smelling plant of the same name. The leaves of the lotus had a soporific[3] effect, however, and the men became forgetful and sleepy. They would have dreamed away the rest of their days had Odysseus not dragged them to the ships and tied them to prevent escape until they were out of range of the strange powers of the lotus.

The next place Odysseus and his men stopped was the island of Cyclopes, who were hideous giants each with an eye in the middle of the forehead. Unknown to the visiting Greeks, the Cyclopes were the children of Poseidon, god of the sea. The Greeks searched the island,

and eventually they reached the cave of Polyphemus. Introducing themselves, they asked for rest and refreshment in the name of Zeus. Had they realized that they were in the domain of those related to Poseidon, they probably would not have mentioned Zeus. The response of Polyphemus to what the Greeks had intended to be a friendly greeting was to scoop up two sailors, tear them to bits with his huge hands, and to eat them raw. The giant then slept soundly through the night. At breakfast he repeated the mealtime performance of the night before. He then took his goats and sheep out of the cave to the mountainside pastures, but was careful to block the entrance with an enormous boulder.

Odysseus, realizing that he could very well lose a pair of his men every time Polyphemus became hungry, knew he had to do something quickly. Escape was impossible because the entrance to the cave was blocked. But Odysseus, ever the tactician, devised a plan. When the giant returned with his herd from the fields, Odysseus had to watch two more sailors turned into dinner. Managing to hide his revulsion[4], the Greek hero offered Polyphemus some vintage wine he had brought with him. The giant downed the wine in great gulps, and his inexperience with the intoxicating beverage proved to be his downfall.

"Tell me your name, stranger," cried Polyphemus "so that I might remember and reward the one who brought me this wonderful wine exceeded only by the nectar of the gods."

Odysseus cleverly replied, "My father and my mother and my comrades all call me No-Man. This is my name. I am No-man."

Just before falling into a deep, drunken sleep, the giant promised that he would leave Odysseus until the very last. "In reward for bringing me this wine," Polyphemus promised Odysseus, "I shall eat all of your men before I devour you."

As soon as Odysseus ascertained that the Cyclops[5] was asleep, he took a long sharpened pole and held its point in the fire until it was glowing hot. Then he plunged the pole into the eye of the giant who awoke blind and in pained rage. His screams were so loud that others of his kind came to the outside of the cave and asked what had happened.

"No-man is hurting me," Polyphemus said again and again in response to his friends' queries. "No-man is hurting me." Believing that Polyphemus had been made mad by the gods, the other Cyclopes went away without even attempting to open the cave.

Odysseus was still faced with the need to escape. No human was strong enough to move the stone from the opening, and even if the stone were moved, the giant sat right there ready to pounce on anyone who tried to pass. The long night passed, and the next morning when the now blind giant moved the rock to let his sheep and goats out he felt the animals as they went by to make sure no humans were among them. Odysseus and each of his men, however, managed to exit the cave tied to the underbelly of a sheep or goat, out of reach of the giant's groping hands.

When Odysseus and his men reached their ships with the furiously enraged giant in hot pursuit, he could not resist one last taunt. "You think that No-Man has been the one to cause you harm. You are wrong. If anyone asks who has blinded Polyphemus, do not say it was No-Man. Say instead it was Odysseus, conqueror of cities and leader of men."

This parting insult further angered Poseidon and added years and many tribulations[6] to the travels of Odysseus before he was finally permitted to return to Ithaca.

Next Odysseus and his men landed at islands ruled by Aeolus, god of the winds. The voyagers were treated hospitably, and upon their departure Aeolus made Odysseus a gift of a securely tied leather pouch which contained all the winds except the one that would guide the ships home. Odysseus warned his men not to touch the pouch, but while he slept they did so and all the winds were set free, forcing the ships once again to contend with them.

The next island on which the men landed was inhabited by cannibals who destroyed eleven of the twelve ships and consumed most of the men. Reduced to one vessel and a small crew, Odysseus sailed on in sadness. The one remaining ship reached a lovely wooded island, where Odysseus sent out a scouting party of men to evaluate whether it would be safe for everyone else to go ashore. When the men did not return, Odysseus realized some disaster had befallen them. Warned by the god Hermes that the island was inhabited by a very beautiful woman who turned men into animals, Odysseus went to see what had happened to his men. He found that Circe, the beautiful woman of whom Hermes spoke, had entertained his men lavishly and then turned them into swine[7]. Hermes had given Odysseus a magic potion to mix in the wine as protection from Circe's enchanting powers. When Circe realized Odysseus was being aided by a god, she turned the men back into their human form and agreed they could leave. Her hospitality was so pleasant, however, that Odysseus and his crew remained on the island for a year before restarting their homeward voyage.

Circe told Odysseus that he would be unable to go back to Ithaca until he had first descended into the depths of Hades. She gave him specific instructions on how he could accomplish this, and he managed to enter the Lower World—even Tartarus where he saw Tantalus, Sisyphus, and Ixion enduring their eternal punishment. He returned to earth, a feat impossible for most mortals.

Surviving a visit to Hades proved to be one of the less difficult aspects of Odysseus' journey. The ship had to pass the Sirens, lovely women whose song lured sailors to their death. Circe had warned Odysseus about the Sirens, however, and he had taken the precaution of stuffing the ears of his crew so they could not hear. After avoiding temptation by the Sirens, the voyagers had to pass between the monsters Scylla and Charybdis who lived one on each side of a narrow stretch of water. Odysseus managed to hold a course that enabled the ship to avoid being sucked into the whirlpool of Charybdis, who several times each day sucked in the sea water before expelling it. To do that, however, he had to pass very close to Scylla, a six-headed monster who grabbed a sailor for each of her mouths. Odysseus had to turn a deaf ear to the cries of his men and sail on, or all would have been lost.

At an island on which grazed the cattle of the god Helios, the sailors stopped to replenish their supplies. Odysseus, after warning his hungry men to eat only the island's fruits and plants and not to touch the sacred cattle then prayed to the gods for guidance. It wasn't long, however, before the smell of roasting meat wafted through the air and Odysseus realized that the men had disobeyed him. As punishment, Zeus sent a terrible storm which wrecked the ship and drowned all but Odysseus.

Odysseus then found himself on the island ruled by the beautiful nymph Calypso. Life was so pleasant there that he remained seven years and was sorely tempted to remain forever. The gods intervened once again, and Hermes was sent to inform Calypso that she must let Odysseus depart. Odysseus, on a raft provided by Calypso, had nearly reached Ithaca when Poseidon discovered him and sent another storm.

The raft was wrecked, and the weary Greek hero had to swim for two days and two nights before being washed up on the shore. Had he not been aided by the goddess Athena, he would surely have perished.

After a brief detour on another island where he was offered the hand of the king's daughter, a lovely young woman named Nausicaa, Odysseus reached his homeland. But his troubles were not yet over. For many years Odysseus was away from home all went smoothly for his faithful wife Penelope and his son Telemachus. But as time went on, more and more suitors sought Penelope not only because she was a beautiful and intelligent woman, but because she controlled vast holdings of property, animals, and human servants.

As the years passed, those attempting to woo Penelope became more and more persistent. Many of them moved into the palace and took over. She refused to marry anyone, however, until she had completed weaving a special garment. She worked diligently on the garment each day, and in the dark of night she unraveled a portion of it so that the work would never be finished.

Odysseus came to his homeland disguised as a beggar. He revealed himself to his son Telemachus and planned how to regain control of his home. His disguise was so good, that only his aged dog, and the woman who had cared for him when he was small were able to recognize him. The men courting Penelope had no idea that the ragged supplicant[8] in their midst was none other than the great Odysseus himself.

One night Penelope appeared to the group of suitors who were becoming more and more agressively demanding that she choose among them. "Here is my husband's bow," she declared as she held up the bow Odysseus had used for hunting many years earlier. "The first of you who is able to bend the bow and use it to hit this target will be my husband."

One man after another tried to bend the bow and failed. Finally the beggar stood up and said "Let me try." Raucous[9] and mocking laughter greeted his offer, but finally the others stepped aside to let the beggar try. With ease he picked up the bow, bent it, and used it with precision[10] to send an arrow into each of the target's marked spots. Odysseus then cooly turned on the suitors and killed many of them. The others trampled each other and died a miserable death in their efforts to flee.

Odysseus was reunited with his wife and son at last, and it was said that they lived in happiness, peace, and prosperity for many years.

[1] **odyssey:** long series of wanderings filled with notable experiences and hardships
[2] **turbulent:** violent
[3] **soporific:** causing or tending to cause sleep
[4] **revulsion:** disgust
[5] **Cyclops:** a one-eyed giant (Cyclops is the singular form of the word Cyclopes)
[6] **tribulations:** grievous troubles or suffering
[7] **swine:** pigs
[8] **supplicant:** beggar
[9] **raucous:** harsh and grating
[10] **precision:** exactness

A CLOSER LOOK

1. What did Odysseus' men do to anger the gods? What were the consequences? Do you think they deserved what they got? Why, or why not?

2. How did the way Odysseus handled his encounter with Polyphemus show that the Greek hero was quite clever? What happened when the hero's pride overshadowed his good judgment?

3. What temptations did Odysseus and his men meet on their long journey? How did they handle them? What were the consequences of what they did?

4. What sort of a person was Penelope? Do you think she and Odysseus had a good marriage? Why, or why not?

● In this poem Telemachus, the son of Ulysses, ponders what would happen if his aging father, "young with the fever of age in his blood—" follows his dreams of adventure to "seek more life."

Maxwell Anderson

TELEMACHUS MUSES

Low in the vale
The haze is hanging.
Green-bright the ocean
Glints and sinks;
With undimmed eyes
I guess on the mountain
The ghost of the storm-cloud
The wraith of the rain.

Down from his crags
The old Ulysses—
Young with the fever
Of age in his blood—
Calls his kings
To the rotten galley;
The madmen follow,
The madman leads.

Dreams are theirs
Of a far adventure;
New Circe's island
And Cyclop's cave:
They have seen death striding
Across their winters;
The flame within them
Gutters and leaps.

Silent, they pass
To the dun-sailed ships,
Bent, white-bearded,
With unfleshed arms:
They seek more life,
But the deep will take them
With storm-clouds rising,
With rain and wind.

● As you read the lines of this famous poem by Alfred Tennyson, imagine what it must have been like for someone like Ulysses to be home from the battles and to have the great adventures be but a memory. What do you think Ulysses has in mind when he says, "Come, my friends, 'tis not too late to seek a newer world..."?

Alfred Tennyson

ULYSSES

It little profits that an idle king,
By this still hearth, among these barren crags,
Matched with an agèd wife, I mete and dole
Unequal laws unto a savage race
That hoard, and sleep, and feed, and know not me.
I cannot rest from travel: I will drink
Life to the lees. All times I have enjoyed
Greatly, have suffered greatly, both with those
That loved me, and alone; on shore, and when
Through scudding drifts the rainy Hyades
Vexed the dim sea. I am become a name;
For always roaming with a hungry heart
Much have I seen and known—cities of men
And manners, climates, councils, governments,
Myself not least, but honored of them all —
And drunk delight of battle with my peers,
Far on the ringing plains of windy Troy.
I am a part of all that I have met;
Yet all experience is an arch wherethrough
Gleams that untraveled world whose margin fades
For ever and for ever when I move.
How dull it is to pause, to make an end,
To rust unburnished, not to shine in use!
As though to breathe were life! Life piled on life
Were all too little, and of one to me
Little remains: but every hour is saved
From that eternal silence, something more,
A bringer of new things; and vile it were
For some three suns to store and hoard myself,
And this gray spirit yearning in desire
to follow knowledge like a sinking star,

Beyond the utmost bound of human thought.
　　This is my son, mine own Telemachus,
To whom I leave the scepter and the isle—
Well-loved of me, discerning to fulfill
This labor, by slow prudence to make mild
A rugged people, and through soft degrees
Subdue them to the useful and the good.
Most blameless is he, centered in the sphere
Of common duties, decent not to fail
In offices of tenderness, and pay
Meet adoration to my household gods,
When I am gone. He works his work, I mine.
　　There lies the port; the vessel puffs her sail:
There gloom the dark, broad seas. My mariners,
Souls that have toiled, and wrought, and thought
　　　　with me, —
That ever with a frolic welcome took
The thunder and the sunshine, and opposed
Free hearts, free foreheads—you and I are old;
Old age hath yet his honor and his toil.
Death closes all; but something ere the end,
Some work of noble note, may yet be done,
Not unbecoming men that strove with gods.
The lights begin to twinkle from the rocks;
The long day wanes; the slow moon climbs; the deep
Moans round with many voices. Come, my friends,
'Tis not too late to seek a newer world.
Push off, and sitting well in order smite
The sounding furrows; for my purpose holds
To sail beyond the sunset, and the baths
Of all the western stars, until I die.
It may be that the gulfs will wash us down;
It may be we shall touch the Happy Isles,
And see the great Achilles, whom we knew.
Though much is taken, much abides; and though
We are not now that strength which in old days
Moved earth and heaven, that which we are, we are—
One equal temper of heroic hearts,
Made weak by time and fate but strong in will
to strive, to seek, to find, and not to yield.

From the Myths

THE ADVENTURES OF AENEAS

● After the fall of Troy, Odysseus was not the only hero of the war who met great adventures as he traveled. Aeneas, one of the heroes of the Trojan side, managed to escape the city and seek a new land. His story was told in the *Aeneid*, the famous Latin poem by Virgil.

O N THE LAST NIGHT OF TROY, AS THE CITY FELL IN flames and ruins, Aeneas dreamed that he was visited by Hector, the great Trojan hero who had just recently been killed. Hector implored Aeneas to take the city's sacred objects and to flee. For a few hours Aeneas tried valiantly to save the city, but he realized that the cause was hopeless.

Unable to save the city, Aeneas decided to save his family. He placed their household gods in the arms of his aged father and hoisted the old man to his shoulders. Taking his young son by the hand, Aeneas hurried to the city gate with his wife Creusa following close behind. By the time the family group reached the area outside the gate, however, Creusa had been separated from the others. Aeneas searched in vain for her and only ceased looking when her ghost appeared to inform him that she had died.

Aeneas and his small band of survivors set up camp near the sea and, over the next year or so, built ships in preparation for the long voyage they knew was to come. Finally Aeneas decided they were ready to sail for their new home, although he knew not for certain where that home would be. Their first stop was the island of Delos, where they consulted

the oracle of Apollo. There they learned that they should establish a home in the country from which their ancestors had first come.

The first place in which Aeneas and his followers attempted to settle was Crete, because they believed their earliest ancestors had come from that place. As they were building their city in Crete, a dreadful pestilence[1] came over the land. Aeneas knew that the gods were warning him that Crete was not the place he was seeking. He was visited one night by figures of the Penates[2] who urged him to abandon Crete and find a true home farther west. Once again the Trojans set sail.

A dreadful storm forced the ships to islands near the western coast of Greece where the Trojans met up with dreadful creatures called Harpies. The Harpies were hideous bird women, each with the heads and torso of a human female, but the wings and claws of a bird of prey.

The Harpies gathered in great flocks whenever the Trojans tried to eat a meal. They shrieked and swooped down to seize whatever they could, and what remained they covered with filth. These horrible creatures were impossible to destroy because their feathers were like the strongest mailcoat[3] which no spear or sword could penetrate. The only solution for Aeneas was to leave that place, and so he did.

The next stop for Aeneas was a harbor on the Greek coast which led him to a city looking remarkably like Troy. There he found Helenus, one of Priam's sons, who had been taken from Troy as a captive but now ruled his new city. Here Aeneas was treated with gracious hospitality. Helenus, who was able to foretell the future, cautioned Aeneas to avoid completely the twin terrors of Scylla and Charybdis by sailing completely around the island of Sicily. Aeneas followed this advice and avoided the fate that befell sailors of Odysseus.

Aeneas was headed for what is now Italy, where he believed that he would eventually found a permanent settlement. Continuing the meddling which she carried out during the long war between Greece and Troy, the goddess Juno (Hera) hoped to keep Aeneas from settling in Italy. She knew that the kingdom founded there would play a major role in the world for generations to come, and she vowed to prevent such an occurrence.

Juno had bribed King Aeolus, god of the winds, to let loose all the storm winds. The resulting chaos then drove ships in many directions. But with the help of Neptune (Poseidon) who did not always see eye to eye with Juno, the ships finally converged on the northern shore of Africa. Aeneas received help from another divinity as well. Venus, who was the mother of Aeneas in addition to being the goddess of love and beauty, came in disguise to her son and told him how to get to the city of Carthage. Venus then cloaked Aeneas in a fog to ensure that no one could see him and cause him harm along the way.

When Aeneas reached Carthage, he found the place ruled by Queen Dido, an extremely beautiful, wise, and courageous woman. Dido, who years earlier had escaped the clutches of an abusive brother in Phoenicia, a land near Syria, received Aeneas with great hospitality. At the instant of their meeting, the cloud surrounding Aeneas was lifted and he was revealed to Dido. The two fell deeply in love, and married secretly. Aeneas seemed content to remain in Carthage and all but forgot his mission to build a new city in Italy. Aeneas finally left Carthage after Mercury brought him an order from Jupiter (Zeus) to do so. Queen Dido, devastated by her loss, immediately died by her own hand. As Aeneas looked back he saw the city in flames. He had no way of knowing that they came from the funeral pyre[4] of his beloved.

Aeneas still had far to go before his voyage was done. He planned to visit the Lower World for the purpose of visiting his father and consulting with him about how to establish a city to carry on the Trojan heritage. Going to Hades and returning was a privilege afforded very few mortals, and Aeneas was aided in this venture by the prophetess Sibyl, who went with him as a guide.

When Aeneas and Sibyl reached the waters of the Acheron, the ferryman Charon already had a full load. But Sibyl begged for space in the boat, and Charon ordered certain ghosts to disembark[5] to make room. In Hades, Aeneas saw the area inhabited by those who had died for love, and he was shocked to see Dido there in the shadows. She did not acknowledge his presence, however, perhaps because she had not yet forgiven him for leaving her.

When Aeneas finally met his father Anchises, the glory and power of what he was about to do was told to him. Aeneas learned that the Roman

Empire, which would be the center of the world for many years, would arise from the settlement he was about to establish in Italy. Fortified by his father's advice, Aeneas returned to the Upper World to complete his mission.

[1] **pestilence:** a deadly epidemic disease (such as bubonic plague)
[2] **Penates:** gods who watched over the home
[3] **mailcoat:** a type of flexible armor
[4] **funeral pyre:** a pile of wood for burning a dead body
[5] **disembark:** get off a boat or ship

A CLOSER LOOK

1. What actions by Aeneas demonstrated commitment to his homeland and the Trojan people? Why do you think he felt the way he did?

2. In what ways were Aeneas and Odysseus similar? In what ways were they different? Use specific examples to support your answers.

3. Why did Aeneas leave Queen Dido? Do you think he should have done so? Why, or why not?

VIII. Myths and Legends of Northern Europe

The ancient people in what is now the northern part of Europe (Scandinavia, Germany, the British Isles) had very much the same questions about the creation of the universe, natural phenomena, and the human condition that their Greek and Roman counterparts to the south did. Their mythology, like that of their southern neighbors, reflects attempts to provide answers to these questions. Their legendary heroes inspired them and gave them hope.

Although the myths and legends of the north have some similarities to those of southern Europe, there are some important differences. Both the gods and the human heroes of the north were vulnerable. It was believed that doom and ultimate destruction were inevitable for gods as well as humans. The greatest virtue, therefore, was considered to be heroism in the face of certain defeat.

Many of the early records and stories of northern Europe were destroyed, but a few glimpses of that ancient world have survived. Among the legendary heroes were Sigurd (or Siegfried, as he was known in the German version of the tale) and Beowulf, who saved the Danes from two hideous monsters.

Every age and culture needs its heroes, and the ancient Celts were no exception. The Celts left no written records directly, but the influence of their presence can be seen in the oral history and legends of Ireland, Wales, Scotland, England and the nearby smaller islands. Perhaps the greatest of the Celtic heroes was King Arthur, who was believed to have ruled Britain at a time when the land was sorely divided and in need of a great leader.

Myths and legends served to entertain and tell a good story as well as to answer important questions about life and the natural world. The Irish have long been known as superb storytellers, and they remain so today, as you will see when you read the retelling of *The Gray Lake*, by Seamus O'Kelly.

From the Myths

MYTHS AND LEGENDS OF THE NORTH

• The myths and legends of northern Europe fulfilled much the same need as did the mythology of the Greeks and Romans. Many of the early records and stories of the northland were destroyed, but a few glimpses of that world have survived. Among the legendary heroes were Sigurd (Siegfried) and Beowulf.

THE EARLY PEOPLES IN WHAT IS NOW THE NORTHERN part of Europe (Scandinavia, Germany, Britain) had questions about the creation of the universe, natural phenomena, and the human condition just as their neighbors to the south did. Their mythology reflects attempts to provide answers to these questions.

Although the myths of the north have some similarities to Greek and Roman myths, there are important differences. Asgard, the home of the gods of the north, was a strange and joyless place which not surprisingly reflected the cold and harsh conditions of the north. Always present in Asgard was the threat of doom which, it was believed, was inevitable[1]. The Greek and Roman gods, however, were believed to be invincible[2] and, furthermore, were expected to indulge in the epitome[3] of the pleasurable life.

Odin, chief of the gods and ruler of the sky, had much the same position in the mythology of the north as Zeus (Jupiter) did in Greek and Roman myths. Unlike Zeus, however, Odin was not interested in the pleasures of life. Zeus and all the other gods of Mount Olympus feasted on ambrosia and nectar[4], but Odin did no such thing. In Valhalla, the great hall of Odin, where the feasts with the heroes of great battles were held, Odin—with the ravens Hugin (Thought) and Munin (Memory) on

his shoulders—presided but did not eat. At the feet of Odin lay his two wolves, Geri and Freki, to whom the god gave any meat set before him.

Each day the ravens, Hugin and Munin, flew over the entire world and returned to report to Odin what they had seen and heard. Those who were invited to the feasts at Valhalla were chosen heroes who had fallen in battle, and no one who had died a peaceful death was deemed worthy. It was said that Odin gathered the bravest to Valhalla so that in the inevitable final contest the bravest would be there in fighting form. Between feasts, the heroes amused themselves by fighting and cutting each other to shreds. At mealtime they recovered, were miraculously made whole, and feasted. To select the heroes who would be invited to Valhalla, Odin sent the Valkyries, messengers who were sometimes referred to as his daughters, to survey battlefields and identify those who had died with special valor, and bring them to Valhalla. The Valkyries were warlike women armed with helmets, shields, and spears. They had strong horses, and it was believed that as they rode along on their mission their armor cast a strange flickering light over the northern skies, making what people called the Aurora Borealis[5], or northern lights.

Beside Odin sat Frigga, his wife. Among the gods were their son Thor (the thunderer), Balder, Bragi, Vigar, and Hoder. Of the other gods, Freyr took care of sunshine and rain, and his sister Freya was the goddess of love. Tyr was the god of battles, and Heimdall was the watchman of the gods. Because it was believed that doom and ultimate destruction were inevitable for both gods and humans alike, the greatest virtue and only possible victory was heroism in the face of certain defeat.

The death of Balder the Good, son of Odin and Frigga, exemplified the inevitability of ultimate destruction. Balder had been tormented with terrible dreams that foretold his destruction, and he told the other gods about what he feared. Frigga exacted an oath from everything she thought could possibly hurt Balder—fire and water, stones, trees, birds and beasts and insects including all that crept or slithered, as well as poisons and every other substance known to cause harm.

The other gods, certain that Frigga's actions were sufficient to protect Balder, amused themselves by using Balder as a target. They aimed rocks, swords, darts, and branches at him in the sincere belief that they would cause no harm. This rather bizarre pastime was considered an honor to Balder and most of the gods enjoyed the game. Loki, known as the creator and perpetrator of evil and fraud as well as milder mischief, was not pleased with the fact that Balder avoided suffering. Balder was virtuous, and Loki disliked him.

Disguised as an old woman, Loki visited Frigga and questioned her about the oaths which were Balder's protection. He found that Frigga had received a promise not to harm Balder from virtually everything except the mistletoe[6]. She had not bothered to pursue the mistletoe because she believed that such a benign[7] plant could do no harm anyway. Armed with this information and a sharpened twig of mistletoe, Loki approached the place where the gods were throwing things at Balder. Off to the side stood Hoder, the blind god who did not participate because he could not see. Loki convinced Hoder to honor Balder by taking part in the sport. He handed the blind god the mistletoe and guided his throw. The missile met its mark, and Balder fell mortally wounded.

A nineteenth century English poet, Matthew Arnold, in a lengthy poem entitled *Balder Dead*, retold the story of the destruction of Balder. The following excerpt from the poem describes the death scene.

Matthew Arnold

LINES FROM BALDER DEAD

So on the floor lay Balder dead; and round
Lay thickly strewn swords, axes, darts, and spears,
Which all the gods in sport had idly thrown
At Balder, whom no weapon pierced or clove;
But in his breast stood fixt the fatal bough
Of mistletoe, which Lok the accuser gave
To Höder, and unwitting Höder threw—
'Gainst that alone had Balder's life no charm.
　　And all the gods and heroes came,
And stood round Balder on the bloody floor,
Weeping and wailing; and Valhalla rang
Up to its golden roof with sobs and cries;
And on the tables stood the untasted meats,
And in the horns and gold-rimmed skulls the wine.
And now would night have fall'n and found them yet
Wailing; but otherwise was Odin's will.

If the gods in Norse mythology were vulnerable, then surely mortals
were even more so. The most revered heroes were always those who had
died violently and valiantly. Sigurd, or Seigfried as he was known in the
German version of the tale was no exception.

　Sigurd courageously killed Fafnir, a most fearsome dragon and,
according to legend, ate of the dragon's heart, then bathed in the beast's
blood in the belief that his body would be rendered invulnerable to any
further danger. Unfortunately, however, a leaf of a linden tree fell on
him and prevented the blood from touching one spot between his
shoulders, and this spot became the hero's Achilles heel[8].

　It was not for the slaying of the dragon that Sigurd was most remembered in literature, however, but for the love story involving Brynhild,
one of the Valkyries, who had disobeyed Odin in some way. As punishment, Brynhild was forced by Odin to sleep surrounded by fire until
awakened by a hero courageous enough to brave the flames. Sigurd rode
through the fire and awakened Brynhild who instantly and joyfully fell

in love with the valiant hero. They did not, however, live happily ever after.

Within a matter of days, Sigurd left Brynhild surrounded by fire as he had found her. He visited the court of the Nibelungs, where he performed many heroic deeds and received much hospitality and honor. Fair Gudren, daughter of the king, was in need of a husband. Her mother, Queen Grimhild, helped things along by administering a magic potion to Sigurd which caused him to lose all recollection of Brynhild. Sigurd wedded Gudren, and it was planned that her brother Gunnar would wed Brynhild. There remained, however, the detail of the flames which guarded Brynhild from all but the bravest. Gunnar wasn't man enough to ride through the fire, but Sigurd asssumed Gunnar's form and performed the task for him. Sigurd then told his wife the whole story.

Brynhild knew she had been deceived, but went through with the marriage to Gunnar as promised. At the wedding feast, the charm of the magic potion wore off, and Sigurd once again looked upon Brynhild with love. The web of deceit complicated the situation beyond redemption, although the two young queens—Gudren and Brynhild—made an effort to get along. They fell out, however, when both claimed the privilege of entering the river to bathe first. In anger, Gudren told Brynhild what Sigurd had confided in her, and the rage of Brynhild was without bounds. She goaded the brother of Gudren into killing Sigurd, and the deed was accomplished by stabbing while Sigurd slept. To complete the inevitable tragedy, Brynhild died by her own hand and shared the funeral pyre of Sigurd.

The German composer, Richard Wagner, used the stories of the Norse gods and heroes as inspiration for the four operas which make up his famous *Ring of the Nibelung*.

Another hero to meet the eventual and inevitable tragedy of doom was Beowulf, subject of a famous epic poem, of the same name. All that is known about *Beowulf*, the only epic poem known to have been written in Old English, was that it was most likely written at some time during the seventh or eighth century. Exactly where, when, and by whom this work was written has remained a mystery.

Beowulf, a youthful prince of the Geats (a tribe in Sweden), sailed to Denmark to help King Hrothgar rid the land of the monster which was destroying the morale of the people along with some of the finest of the king's men. After his successful bout with the monster Grendel in the king's hall, Beowulf next took on Grendel's mother. He survived his journey to the monster's lair at the bottom of a murky lake, and emerged triumphant. Beowulf then returned to Sweden where he ruled his people in harmony for half a century. But, as in every other instance of a legendary hero of that time and place, Beowulf's end contained a large measure of sadness and doom. While slaying a fire dragon that had been ravaging his land, Beowulf's cries to his comrades for assistance went unheeded. The hero killed the dragon, but while doing so received a mortal wound and was lost.

[1] **inevitable:** certain to happen; not able to be avoided
[2] **invincible:** not able to be beaten or conquered
[3] **epitome:** typical example
[4] **ambrosia and nectar:** special food and drink of the gods
[5] **Aurora Borealis:** lights caused by meteoric activity (also known as "northern lights") appearing in the night sky of the northern hemisphere
[6] **mistletoe:** a parasitic plant with yellow flowers and white berries (now used as a Christmas decoration)
[7] **benign:** kindly; not harmful
[8] **Achilles heel:** vulnerable spot so-called because the mother of Greek hero Achilles held her infant son by the heel and dipped him in the River Styx so he would be invulnerable and immortal. He was eventually killed by a Trojan arrow to the heel in the spot left unprotected because of his mother's thumb.

A CLOSER LOOK

1. In what ways were the gods and heroes of the north different from the gods and heroes of Greece and Rome? Why do you think this was so?

2. Who was Balder? How and why did he die? What is your opinion of the conduct of his comrades? Do you think there is any lesson to be learned from his story? If so, what is it? Explain and give reasons for your response.

3. Who was Sigurd? What were his strong points? What, if any, were his weaknesses? Do you think he got what he deserved? Why, or why not?

4. Who was Beowulf? What did he accomplish that made him a hero? How and why did he die?

Mabel Louise Robinson

KING ARTHUR'S PLACE IN THE WORLD

● Every age and culture needs its heroes, and a man named Arthur was believed to have become King of Britain at a time when that troubled land was greatly in need of a leader. This selection by Mabel Louise Robinson explains the role the legends of King Arthur play in literature and in life.

BACK IN THE SIXTH CENTURY THE BRITISH ISLES were not as they are now. England, Ireland, Scotland, Wales, all were divided up into small kingdoms each with its own ruler, each looking for trouble. They fought together, won or lost their lands, shifted their boundaries, until, as one writer says, we need the magic of Merlin to set us straight about the places. On the island of Great Britain the conditions under which human beings lived were much the same in all of the kingdoms. Most of the people were poor beyond belief, and moreover they had no possible way of escaping from that plight of poverty. They were in a complete state of slavery to the rich.

Naturally enough, among the rich there was a constant struggle for power. The poor worked for them so that they had nothing else to do except to increase their riches. All their power lay in the amount of wealth to which they could lay claim.

Since they could not come by their wealth by hard work because the poor released them from that necessity, there was of course no way of increasing riches except by seizing each other's property. And since no one would allow his property to be taken from him without protest, the struggle for possession kept men fighting. Their real work was fighting and they did it with pleasure. Their reward was more lands which sooner or later somebody would take away from them. Their honors were all based on skill with the sword.

Out of this constant struggle, and the honors and wealth attached to victory, were bound to arise certain standards. Because the strong could win the battle, there was a real worship of physical strength. There was no place in the world for the weak of body even if the mind was strong. The dependence upon the sword for power meant dependence upon enough strength to wield it. For this a man did not need judgment and wisdom as much as he needed blind courage and brawn.

Then because of the standards which worshipped strength there was no need or demand for that high quality of living, Justice. To decide upon the justice of a matter we try to weigh and consider all sides of it. Then we make a decision. Here there was no time for thinking. The sword must be drawn instantly or all was lost.

So the downtrodden, suffering poor remained downtrodden and suffering, and expected nothing else. The rich stayed arrogant and overbearing, and there was no one to protest. Between them was a gulf so wide and so deep that no one in his or her right mind would try to cross it.

When things become too unbearable we usually look for help, and expect to find it in some leader. It may be a new President, or king or queen, or leader of religion, but it must be somebody new and strong and wise, somebody who has our interests at heart. To such a person we give our support. About such a person we like to hear stories and to tell them. We build up around that person the kind of good life which we want to believe is true.

So back in the sixth century the need arose for help in lightening the pressure of the unbearable conditions. The downtrodden come to the point where they realize that they must have help or go out of existence. When in those early days a strong chieftain appeared in England, the people rallied around him, took him into their hearts as their deliverer, and began as we do, to build up around him stories of power and magic. This was their tribute to his defense of them.

This leader was a person of great strength and humanity, a combination so unusual that it is no wonder the people loved him. He helped to unite the small kingdoms, and thus gave them security. He held back the invading Saxons, and thus gave the Britains time to develop their own culture. He led them to victories in Europe, and thus made them proud of their strength. Whether his name was Arthur does not matter. Arthur is the name by which we know him.

If it seemed unreasonable later that such a chieftain could have achieved so much success, the story-teller added a little magic to make the story believable. And so as the years rolled by, the wonder at the prowess[1] of Arthur increased. The stories caught the imagination of the people from century to century. Always there has been need of help, always the hope of finding it.

Because there were no printed books back in the fifth and sixth centuries when these events were supposed to have happened, the stories were circulated by telling and by minstrel[2] singing. It is easy to see how the narrator might add a rich detail here and there to heighten the interest of his audience. Such improvements are not limited to the sixth century.

Curiously enough, this way of telling stories seemed to afford a wider circulation than books achieve. All over the world are these stories of the great chieftain, King Arthur, in every language. The French took over the story, and later we have their special line on it, the book of Crestien of Troyes. He added French qualities to the stories but he used Britain for the scenes and the events.

Even out in Turkey I have found traces of the Arthurian legends. Years ago when I was teaching in Constantinople College, an English girl invited me to her home on the Black Sea for Easter holidays. Her father was head of all the life-saving stations on the Black Sea, and she had been born and brought up there. She spoke Turkish like a native, and as we walked along the shore she often stopped to talk to the fishermen and boatmen.

One day an old Turk began a long tale. "What is he talking about?" I asked idly. She laughed. "It is an old story he always loves to tell and he wants me to tell you."

"What is it about?" I inquired.

"Oh, just about a sword coming up out of the water out there." She pointed out to the water which was so blue that I thought it should be called the Blue Sea.

She could hardly believe my excitement, but she got the old man to tell the story and translated it word for word. It was the King Arthur tale of the arm clothed in white samite[3] rising out of the water with the gleaming sword in its hand. It was a King Arthur tale told by an old Turk who could neither read nor write, and who had never been away from the shore of the Black Sea.

Where did he get it? Oh, his father, his grandfather, any good Turk who lived here could tell that story. And he was much pleased to find somebody who wanted to listen to it. What invaders, perhaps the Crusaders, had carried the story, or how it originated, I never knew. But I did know from that moment how wide and how deep was the distribution of Arthurian tales.

At last when people began to read and write, the stories took their place in print. And there they have been ever since. In the middle of the twelfth century the women especially began to demand romance. By the next century the romance plots were in full swing. Someone has called the Arthurian romance the world's first great novel. If the plots sometimes sounded like fairy tales, their essence reflected the society of the time. Small wonder, then, as a famous Arthurian scholar has remarked, that you cannot expect consistency in Arthurian romance.

It was the Age of Chivalry which drew its sustenance[4] from the King Arthur tales. Again as time had swung its great arcs of the centuries over the earth, the Middle Ages came along with as downtrodden and suffering poor as ever existed. Conditions were so bad that people looked forward to the destruction of the earth, to the burning of the world and the fall of heaven upon it. It seemed better to die than to live in such torment.

But now in this everlasting rhythm of humanity's efforts to better itself, the ideals of knighthood began to lighten the darkness. The warring knights took over some responsibility for their vassals. They began to use their strength in the service of the weak and oppressed. They protected women and surrounded them with sentimental ideals which they wove into stories. They started an era of greater consideration for the dignity of the human race.

From the middle of the eleventh century to the end of the fourteenth, the Middle Ages struggled to pull itself out of the slime. The King Arthur ideals contributed more help, perhaps, than we can measure. Knighthood became a responsible state not to be undertaken lightly.

The preparation for it began in childhood. At seven the son of a nobleman became a page at some castle or in the court. Until he was fourteen his schooling was all concerned with principles of knighthood, protection of others, obedience to his betters, the truths of religion. Not a bad foundation for youth to grow upon!

Then at fourteen he became a squire, and that meant a strict training in horsemanship, in how to behave among the knights and ladies, and in the implements of war.

At twenty-one his training was over. With impressive rites he was formally made a knight. His armor and his sword marked him as a man grown, ready to face the troubles of the world. He swore to defend the weak and the poor, to be loyal to the king and the church, to avoid any form of slander, to love and marry one maiden only, and to be true to his own word. Even if no human being in those days could live up to such promises, he had at least taken a step in the right direction.

Through the years came the records of knightly ideals in books, for printing had now become a means of communication. They served to spread more widely the new doctrines of civilization. Geoffrey of Monmouth began with a Latin history of King Arthur which probably few people could read. But it was translated into English and French, and so the foundation was laid in the twelfth century.

From that time on, the stories of King Arthur became part of the heritage of the race. When in 1470 Sir Thomas Malory wrote his classic, LE MORTE D'ARTHUR, he gave the world in permanent form the story of King Arthur and his knights. And to this day, the book is interesting reading. Beneath its archaic[5] style are drama and emotion. Its fine, difficult print blazed with the light of truth. It is art, and history, and beyond everything to people in those dark days, a stimulus to right living. The influence of King Arthur and his knights on the human race is beyond measure.

Modern youth may well ask, "How much of this story can I believe?" For in these days of science we ask for proof of what people say. Yet perhaps these old story-tellers were wiser than they knew. They may have added magic for effect, but they incorporated into it a kind of symbolism which is eternally true.

The sword could be drawn out of the stone by one person only, and

that person had to be the right one. Not strength of muscle was necessary, for Arthur was only a boy. But behind his physical effort must lie strength of spirit such as none other possessed. Would that we might always test our leaders by some such magic!

There may not have been a shining silver chalice which had served the Lord's Last Supper and which now could cause miracles to happen. But the Holy Grail serves as the symbol of the aim toward which the pure in heart strive. An end which is not concerned with personal gain, with money or with fame, but with the beauty of the spirit. The churches take it over, and struggling humanity keeps its eyes on the shining goal.

The Round Table itself may be a kind of symbol of unity and equality. It had no head nor foot where the greatest or least must take his seat. These knights sat about a Table Round where each man's place was graven with his name. Just as today each member of the Cabinet has his or her nameplate on the back of the chair. They could look each other in the eye, and catch each shadow of thought and feeling. Their justice was the product of united effort.

So through these tales of King Arthur runs a lovely symbolism which deepens the interest and adds richness of content as we work it out while we read. And here we have another contribution of King Arthur and his knights to the landmarks of the world.

[1] **prowess:** exceptional ability and bravery
[2] **minstrel:** medieval musician who sang or recited stories to the accompaniment of music
[3] **samite:** a heavy silk fabric sometimes interwoven with gold worn in the Middle Ages
[4] **sustenance:** nourishment; means of sustaining life
[5] **archaic:** marked by the characteristics of an earlier period; antiquated

A CLOSER LOOK

1. How were the problems people faced in the time of King Arthur different from those people have in today's world? In what ways are things the same? Explain using specific examples.

2. What was the role of women during the Age of Chivalry? How did the role of women differ from that of men?

3. How are the legends of King Arthur like the Greek and Roman myths? Are there any contemporary heroes who might someday be as important as King Arthur? Why do you think so?

4. Do you think the ideals of knighthood would be valid in today's world. Why, or why not?

● As you read these lines by the nineteenth century Irish poet Arthur O'Shaughnessy, try to get a sense of the ages of history and the empires which have come and gone.

Arthur O'Shaughnessy

ODE

We are the music-makers
    And we are the dreamers of dreams,
Wandering by lone sea-breakers,
    And sitting by desolate streams;—
World-losers and world-forsakers,
    On whom the pale moon gleams;
Yet we are the movers and shakers
    Of the world for ever, it seems.

With wonderful deathless ditties
We build up the world's great cities,
    And out of a fabulous story
    We fashion an empire's glory:
One man with a dream, at pleasure,
    Shall go forth and conquer a crown;
And three with a new song's measure
    Can trample an empire down.

We, in the ages lying
    In the buried past of the earth,
Built Nineveh[1] with our sighing,
    And Babel[2] itself with our mirth;
And o'erthrew them with prophesying,
    To the old of the new world's worth;
For each age is a dream that is dying,
    Or one that is coming to birth.

[1] **Nineveh:** an ancient capital of Assyria; its ruins can be found on the banks of the Tigris River
[2] **Babel:** an ancient biblical city in which a tower intended to reach the heavens was begun, and the confusion of languages occurred (See *Genesis*, Chapter XI)

Seamus O'Kelly
(retold by Annie Mueser)

THE GRAY LAKE

● The ancient myths represented efforts to explain natural phenomena and the human condition, but they were far more as well. Perhaps most important, the myths were wonderful and entertaining stories. You need not take Seamus O'Kelly's explanation for the origin of Loughrea at face value, but you can learn something about people as you enjoy this retold tale.

L ONG AND LONG AGO, THERE WAS A SLEEPY LITTLE town snuggled in amongst the hills in what is now the west of Ireland. The town was renowned for seven of the purest springs of water that ever sparkled anywhere. In fact, these springs were so famous that the town itself was called Seven Sisters.

The townspeople constructed a great and costly well around the springs. A heavy leaden lid of a most unusual design was installed over the well, and every evening at sundown this great lid was lowered and locked on the well by means of a secret lock and a secret key.

Between each evening's sunset and the following day's dawn, the springs became extraordinarily active. And because each night brought with it the possibility that the valley might be flooded and its people and animals drowned, the covering and locking of the well became a ritual of extreme importance.

The most famous person in the town of the Seven Sisters was the Keeper of the Key. Although, of course, he did have a name, he was known to one and all simply as the Keeper of the Key. His appearance befitted his important station in life. He always looked dignified and appropriately arrogant. His white silk knee-breeches, his green swallow-tail coat, and his hat cocked at just the precisely proper angle, were always impeccable.[1] The image of a key and seven sprays of water was embroidered on his coat sleeve in an intricate design fashioned with gold threads.

The Keeper of the Key lived in a great mansion and this mansion was almost as famous as the seven springs. People travelled from afar to see the mansion and marvel at its grandeur. Leading to the great oak door was a flight of green marble steps, each one carried from the Connemara mountains and polished by the hands of many men. On the door was a remarkable knocker and doorknob made of hammered gold. The knocker, not surprisingly, was in the shape of a key. The door knob was seven golden water nymphs.

Every morning a fanfare of trumpets greeted the day. An armed guard moved from the courtyard to the foot of the marble steps, and a second fanfare of trumpets blared while the great oaken door swung open. Out would come the Keeper of the Key who, upon personally pulling the door shut by means of the famous knob, would then descend the steps. He next would be escorted to the springs, where even at such an early hour many would be waiting. The townspeople always stood at the respectful and required distance of fifty yards, while the Keeper of the Key opened the lid so the business of the day could begin.

After opening the well every morning, the Keeper of the Key would march back to the mansion, ascend the marble steps, open the great door, and disappear inside. Every evening, just before sundown, the closing of the well occurred with similar ceremony. Again, the people would keep their appointed distance while the Keeper of the Key performed his task. Then the town crier would go from street to street exclaiming, "The lock is on the seven sisters, and all is well!"

And so this ritual of the opening and the closing of the well was repeated day after day, week after week, and year after year. But there was something that seemed quite odd to one and all. No one—not anyone anywhere—had, to the best of anyone's knowledge, ever seen the Key. And while this added to the awe in which many held the Keeper of the Key, it also provoked some resentment.

The mystery of where the Keeper kept the Key even led to a saying in common use around Ireland. When a man had an object or property to which he had doubtful title, his neighbors were likely to gossip behind his back and say, "He got it where the Keeper gets the Key." And this was not a compliment!

Part II

As time went on, and each day passed, more and more people became vexed with the Keeper of the Key. They still respected his position and the essential, although not fully understood role he played with respect to their security. They resented his power, however, and some even tried—without success—to ascertain the secret of the key.

The Keeper of the Key, who never mingled with the masses, was the subject of much conversation. And frequently that conversation turned to the topic of the man's daughter, a young maiden who often stood beside her father on the watchtower. The girl, who was never allowed to leave the mansion without escort, lived as a virtual prisoner. She was courted by many, but no suiter ever got beyond the door. The Keeper of the Key dismissed with anger any man audacious[2] enough to venture to the mansion and seek the girl's hand. Those who lived in the town pitied the girl who, it had been said, was protected by her father as a pearl might be kept from the world by the oyster's shell. Their pity was largely wasted on the daughter of the Keeper of the Key. She was not discontented, because not only did she love her father, but she knew of no other way to live.

One day things began to change for the daughter of the Keeper of the Key. She was sitting, as she was often wont to do, at the window painting a little picture. Suddenly the clear call of a passing shepherd boy caught her ear. "How up! How up! How up!" he called to his flock as he drove them past the mansion's window on his way to the market. The girl looked out the window at the source of the sound. At that same moment the shepherd boy happened to look up. His eyes caught hers and they both smiled. The boy moved on with his sheep. "How up! How up! How up!" he continued to call as he went happily on his way.

That evening the Keeper of the Key and his daughter went for a stroll through the town of the Seven Sisters. The people they met bowed in respect, and stepped back so the two could pass. Among those they met was the shepherd boy. Once again the shepherd's boy's eyes caught the girl's glance. And later that night, when the shepherd boy should have returned home to the hills of Sunnach from whence he had come, he

170

elected not to do so. And the next night and the next and the next also found him in the town of the Seven Sisters. By day he wandered about the town and made many trips by the mansion's window while he called to an imaginary flock. Each time he passed the window he was greeted with the wave of a delicate hand. At night he retired to a tiny rented room and wrote poems of love to the daughter of the Keeper of the Key.

Before long, the Keeper of the Key began to wonder what was going on with this shepherd boy who seemed to be spending an inordinate[3] amount of time loitering about the mansion. When he observed the lad calling to imaginary sheep, the Keeper of the Key suspected the worst. "The people from the country hills have come to overthrow me," he thought. And before another day had passed, the shepherd found himself in prison waiting to be banished from the land.

When the daughter of the Keeper of the Key realized what had happened to her beloved shepherd boy, she tearfully told her father the truth. The Keeper of the Key was relieved that the boy had not been sent to steal the key or make other such mischief. He did not, however, take kindly to the fact that the lad had been bold enough to approach the young maiden. The punishment he ordered for the shepherd boy was a public dipping—seven times—in the well of the Seven Sisters. The girl pleaded for mercy for her love, but the Keeper of the Key refused to yield. "Ipse dixit,[4]" he sternly said. "It has been spoken."

A great crowd gathered at the well to witness the public humiliation and punishment of the shepherd boy. The boy was tied and lowered by servants of the Keeper of the Key into the well. The well shaft was cold and creepy, dark and dank, and the shepherd boy was certain of his doom.

Then a most remarkable thing happened. As fast as the servants let out the rope to lower the lad into the water the Seven Sisters moved lower. They lapped at the boy's heels, but did not harm him. Then, when the rope was fully extended, the servants jerked it up and down the prescribed seven times. The people who had gathered to revel in another's misfortune cheered and clapped. But all was not lost for the gentle shepherd boy whose love poems had captured the attention of the Seven Sisters.

The spirits of the Seven Sisters spoke to the boy. "O shepherd boy," they said, "we too have been harmed by the Keeper of the Key, and we seek your help even as we offered you our own. We were not created to spend our nights pent up in this unnatural shaft. We want to be free, and leap about and meet our lover, the moon. At night he calls, but we are restrained underneath the locked lid of the well. You can set us free."

"I would love to set you free," replied the shepherd boy, "but I have no way to do that. The Keeper of the Key is the only one who knows how to open the lid. And I would have no way of knowing how to make his magic."

"We know his secret, and we will share it with you," said the spirits of the Seven Sisters. "Promise to set us free and we will tell you the secret of the key. And as your reward, you shall have the hand of the daughter of the Keeper of the Key."

The shepherd boy promised the spirits of the Seven Sisters he would set them free, and they passed on the secret of the key to him. "The Keeper of the Key," they said, "is not the fine, noble gentleman he appears to be. Inside his soul lurks the devil himself. He has on his hands the blood of the five goldsmiths who designed the water nymph doorknob. He arranged the death of these five because they, of course, knew the secret of the key. But we also know that secret and now pass it on to you."

"While pulling the door after him, the Keeper of the Key simply touches the third toe of the fourth water nymph three times in rapid beat. This shoots the key into his coatsleeve. In order to return the key to its secret place, he presses the second toe of the third nymph. That's all there is to it."

"I'll set you free," promised the shepherd boy to the spirits of the Seven Sisters. And before they could reply, the servants of the Keeper of the Key pulled on the ropes and drew the boy out of the well. The Seven Sisters splashed the lad gently as he rose to the surface to give him the appearance of having suffered fully from immersion and the indignities of his dipping. The spectators clapped and shouted.

Part III

The shepherd boy lay on the ground with his eyes closed. The crowd began to move away. But some had pity on the lad. An old peasant woman in a hooded cloak hobbled to his side and bent over him. She smoothed back his hair and gently stroked his cheek. The shepherd boy opened his eyes and saw that the old woman was really the daughter of the Keeper of the Key in disguise. He told her he would come to the door at midnight and that she should divert the guards in some way. He told her to listen for the shepherd's call.

At midnight he gave the call. The guards moved away from the door, and he could see that they were in the courtyard taking sips from overflowing wine goblets. The boy ran to the door and pressed three times on the third toe of the fourth water nymph. A little golden key was propelled into his hand. He ran down the stairs and went at top speed to the well. He could hear the Seven Sisters twisting and straining to get out.

"O Seven Sisters," cried the shepherd boy. "I have come to give you to your lover."

The moans of pain from the Seven Sisters quickly turned into cries of joy and anticipation. The shepherd boy put the key in the lock, turned it, and immediately caused the lid to revolve away from the mouth of the well. The Seven Sisters laughed and leaped and danced in the light of the moon. The shepherd boy could see seven spirals of clear water which, in the moonlight, sparkled and took the shapes of nymphs lovelier even than those of his dreams and poems.

The shepherd boy turned and ran, because the water was already rushing through the streets of the town. People left their houses and trampled each other in their haste to flee the rising waters. When the shepherd boy reached the mansion the guards were leaving the court-yard with trumpets blaring. In the doorway stood the Keeper of the Key with one hand holding a candle and the other pressing the water nymph to release the key which, of course, was no longer in the doorknob. In desperation the Keeper of the Key began to run to the well, but he was driven back by the waves of water and people running for their lives.

The shepherd boy ascended the steps of the mansion and gave his call. "How up! How up! How up!" The fair damsel heard his call and came to him. The boy told her what had happened, and said he would take her to the safety of the hills.

"I must be with my father at the well," she answered. "I am the daughter of the Keeper of the Key. I must be with him in his time of trouble." As she looked toward the drawbridge and what was left of the town beyond, she began to feel faint. The water was eagerly consuming everything in its path—people, animals, structures—everything.

"*I* am the Keeper of the Key," said the shepherd boy, holding up the gold key. "Come with me." He swept the girl into his arms and headed for the hills. Behind him the terrible waters swirled and reared and roared in an orgy of destruction. Not a human creature escaped that night except the shepherd boy and the damsel he carried in his arms. Every time the waters came near the boy, the swirling waves reared up like great horses and then fell back. Again and again the pursuing waters backed off just enough to enable the two to reach the safety of the hills. But everyone else from the town of the Seven Sisters perished.

The shepherd boy looked back at the town one last time, and all he could see was the very top of the mansion's watch tower. Standing on it was the Keeper of the Key, with his arms outstretched and face staring at the swollen moon. And, as the story tells, the seven water nymphs strangely glimmered in the moonlight and leaped about the man just before he vanished.

As dawn approached, the activity of the water gradually diminished and the passions of the wild night were finally exhausted. The sun rose in the east, and the shepherd boy drew the damsel to his side. Hand in hand they faced the new day. Not a trace of the town of the Seven Sisters remained.

"Look," cried the shepherd boy, "at Loch Riabhach!" And then he drew his arm back and hurled the secret key into the far waters of the lake. There, as far as anyone knows, it still lies today. And the shepherd boy and his bride founded a new town beside the lake. That town and the lake survive still. You can see for yourself if you ever happen to be in County Galway in the west of Ireland. Just look for Loughrea (or, as it is known in Irish, Baile Loch Riabhach) — the town of the Gray Lake.

[1] **impeccable:** faultless
[2] **audacious:** extremely bold
[3] **inordinate:** not within proper limits
[4] **ipse dixit:** he himself said it (Latin)

A CLOSER LOOK

1. Who was the Keeper of the Key? What was he like? Why did some of the townspeople resent him?

2. When people said, "He got it where the Keeper gets the Key," what do you think they meant?

3. Why did the Keeper of the Key keep his daughter away from everyone? Do you think he was wrong to do so? Why do you think she and the shepherd boy were attracted to each other?

4. What natural phenomena did the story of the Gray Lake attempt to explain? Are there any earlier myths that have similarities?

● Even for someone who believes, creatures such as fairies or the so-called little people may be very hard to see. Let your imagination help you travel through the following lines and help you experience the imagery.

Jessica Nelson North

WHERE DO THE FAIRIES MEET?

Where, oh where, do the fairies meet?
   I've hunted the country through;
I've looked in the heart of the violet sweet
   As it shone with its wealth of dew,
And I've watched the crest of a cloudland fleet
   As it floated across the blue.

I've searched the sky when the thunder
   rolled,
   By the wrestling demons riven;
And I've watched the lights of red and gold
   As they shone in the west at even,
And the still white beams, so clear and cold,
   That fell from the moon in heaven.

I thought, as I stood on the silent hill,
   That I heard their hastening feet;
But it was the wind of midnight chill
   As it rustled the fields of wheat.
And the question remains unanswered still, —
   Where do the fairies meet?

IX. Mythology Today

O f what use to modern people are the myths of ancient Greece and Rome? Are the myths really relevant to human concerns of today? As the illustration at the left might suggest, problems and troubles abound in the world, and have for a very long time. The explanation for the world's current troubles, of course, cannot be attributed to the tale of Pandora. But there may be messages in certain myths that are worth pondering even today.

The story of Pegasus and Bellerophon, for example, may be read quite simply as a fantastic mythological tale of a winged horse and a hero who used that horse to do amazing things. But the symbolism of the winged horse may also contain a lesson.

Albert Camus, a twentieth century Frenchman, wrote extensively on what he considered to be the absurdity of the human condition. One of his best known short essays, *The Myth of Sisyphus*, is based on the ancient Greek myth in which Sisyphus was punished by being condemned to push a huge stone uphill over and over again thoughout eternity.

Throughout today's world—in language, literature, science, art, music,—examples of the influence of classical mythology can be found. One cannot be a truly educated person without some understanding of the contributions made to our language and culture by the ancient Greeks and Romans. From great poetry to advertising symbols and slogans, the influence of mythology remains strong. With William Wordsworth, in his poem *The Excursion*, for example, we can imagine how mythology in ancient Greece began. "Beauty is truth, truth beauty...." says poet John Keats, in *Ode on a Grecian Urn*, a work which was inspired by classical mythology.

Myths and the symbols they use are not simply of the past. Fleet-footed Hermes, for example, symbolizes the world wide delivery network of florists. Until recently, drivers purchased gas and oil from coast to coast at the sign of the flying red horse, and anyone who takes a journey by car is likely to make use of an Atlas.

From the Myths

PEGASUS AND BELLEROPHON

● Bellerophon dreamed that he might have the great winged horse Pegasus, and his dream came true. With the help of the steed, Bellerophon was able to accomplish great deeds which repaid his debt to society for certain wrongs he had committed. But his ambition exceeded his rightful grasp.

BELLEROPHON WAS AN AMBITIOUS AND BOLD young man believed by most who knew him to be the son of Glaucus, King of Corinth. Glaucus, like his father Sisyphus before him, had managed to offend the gods most gravely. Glaucus was a horseman of considerable note, and it was said that he fed his horses human flesh to make them stronger and more warlike in battle. Such a hideous practice was dealt with by the gods in like manner. Glaucus was thrown from his chariot, torn to bits by his own steeds, and devoured on the spot.

Bellerophon was a handsome young man who loved horses and longed for Pegasus, the winged horse which was believed to have sprung from the blood of the Gorgon shed when Perseus killed that horrible monster. Pegasus was a most magnificent animal with wonderful and extraordinary powers. Even though some thought Bellerophon might actually be the son of Poseidon, god of horsemanship as well as god of the sea, taming Pegasus was not something the young man could accomplish on his own.

Bellerophon's mother had been taught by Athena herself, and it was to the goddess of wisdom that the young man finally turned. Bellerophon went to Athena's temple to pray and stay by the altar for as long as it took until the goddess responded to his prayers. When he was deep

in sleep, Athena came to him in his dreams. She held out a golden object, and when he reached for it the goddess disappeared. Bellerophon woke with a start, and in his hand was a golden bridle unlike any he had ever seen. Bellerophon had never before been able to approach the winged horse, but with the help of Athena he was able to walk right up to the animal and put on the bridle. Soon Bellerophon was riding Pegasus through the air, and the winged horse's feet only touched the ground upon command.

Bellerophon's life became somewhat complicated, but the myths do not provide all the details. It was said that Bellerophon had somehow killed his brother, although the circumstances were never fully explained. It was necessary, therefore, for the young man to do penance and be purified. King Proetus of Argos purified him, but during the time Bellerophon was a guest in that kingdom, the wife of Proetus, whose name was Anteia, fell in love with the young man. When Bellerophon rejected her advances, Anteia told her husband that Bellerophon had done her wrong and should be punished by death.

Proetus was unwilling to kill someone who had shared his home and table as a guest. Such an action would tend to anger many of the gods, and would be especially displeasing to Zeus. The king came up with an alternate plan, however, which he expected to have the same effect. He asked Bellerophon to carry a letter to the King of Lycia, a place far off in Asia. The journey was readily possible with the help of Pegasus, and Bellerophon undertook the task willingly. In Lycia, the king entertained Bellerophon royally for several days before reading the letter which asked that he kill the young man. He was unwilling to do so, of course, because Bellerophon had already been a guest in his home and he did not wish to incur the wrath of Zeus.

Instead, the Lycian ruler sent Bellerophon on a mission to kill the Chimaera, a terrible creature which was part lion, part serpent, and part goat. In addition to having the most fearsome qualities of both lion and snake, the Chimaera had a fiery breath of flames which could not be quenched. Anyone who got close to the creature ran the almost insurmountable risk of being burned to death. Bellerophon, however, had no such fears. He simply flew over the monster on Pegasus and managed to slay the Chimaera with little effort.

Bellerophon returned to King Proetus who by that time had realized that dispatching this young man was easier said than done. Each time the King sent Bellerophon on a task that would have killed an ordinary man, Bellerophon and Pegasus were successful. Finally Proetus made peace with Bellerophon and even gave him the hand of his daughter in marriage.

Unfortunately for Bellerophon, he was not willing to keep his achievements in proper perspective. He became arrogant and overly ambitious, and behaved as if he were above his fellow mortals. One day he attempted to ride Pegasus up Mount Olympus in an effort to sit with the gods. Pegasus was unwilling to ascend the mountain of the deities, however, and he threw Bellerophon to the ground. Bellerophon wandered the earth in disgrace, on foot, until he died.

Pegasus, looked on with favor by the gods, was invited to share the royal stables of Olympus. This time the horse knew he was meant to fly to the home of the gods, and so he did. He took his place with the other steeds of Zeus, and was the chosen horse to bring the thunder and lightning of the great god any time Zeus wished to use his thunderbolt.

A CLOSER LOOK

1. How had Bellerophon's father offended the gods? What was his punishment? Do you believe the punishment was appropriate? Why, or why not?

2. Why did Bellerophon dream of owning Pegasus? How did his dream come true? In what way did his life change after he acquired the winged horse?

3. Why did Proetus wish to kill Bellerophon? Why didn't he do so? What did Proetus do instead? How did the winged horse save Bellerophon?

4. Why did Bellerophon try to ride Pegasus up Mount Olympus? What happened? What lesson, if any, might be learned from that story?

Eleanor Farjeon

PEGASUS

From the blood of Medusa
Pegasus sprang.
His hoof of heaven
Like melody rang.
His whinny was sweeter
Than Orpheus' lyre,
The wing on his shoulder
Was brighter than fire.

His tail was a fountain,
His nostrils were caves,
His mane and his forelock
Were musical waves,
He neighed like a trumpet,
He cooed like a dove,
He was stronger than terror
And swifter than love.

He could not be captured,
He could not be bought,
His rhythm was running,
His standing was thought.
With one eye on sorrow
And one eye on mirth
He galloped in heaven
And gambolled on earth.

And only the poet
With wings to his brain
Can mount him and ride him
Without any rein,
The stallion of heaven
The steed of the skies,
The horse of the singer
Who sings as he flies.

Albert Camus

THE MYTH OF SISYPHUS

● Sisyphus was condemned by the gods to spend eternity pushing a huge rock to the top of a mountain, only to have it fall back each time. In this modern essay by Albert Camus, you will have a chance to ponder the fate of Sisyphus. Is Sisyphus, the absurd hero, a tragic figure?

THE GODS HAD CONDEMNED SISYPHUS TO CEASE-lessly rolling a rock to the top of a mountain, whence the stone would fall back of its own weight. They had thought with some reason that there is no more dreadful punishment than futile and hopeless labor.

If one believes Homer, Sisyphus was the wisest and most prudent of mortals. According to another tradition, however, he was disposed to practice the profession of highwayman.[1] I see no contradiction in this. Opinions differ as to the reasons why he became the futile laborer of the underworld. To begin with, he is accused of a certain levity[2] in regard to the gods. He stole their secrets. Ægina, the daughter of Æsopus, was carried off by Jupiter. The father was shocked by that disappearance and complained to Sisyphus. He, who knew of the abduction, offered to tell about it on condition that Æsopus would give water to the citadel of Corinth. To the celestial thunderbolts he preferred the benediction of water. He was punished for this in the underworld. Homer tells us also that Sisyphus had put Death in chains. Pluto could not endure the sight of his deserted, silent empire. He dispatched the god of war, who liberated Death from the hands of her conquerer.

It is said also that Sisyphus, being near to death, rashly wanted to test his wife's love. He ordered her to cast his unburied body into the middle of the public square. Sisyphus woke up in the underworld. And there, by an obedience so contrary to human love, he obtained from Pluto permission to return to earth in order to chastise his wife. But when he had seen again the face of this world, enjoyed water and sun, warm stones and the sea, he no longer wanted to go back to the infernal darkness. Recalls, signs of anger, warnings were of no avail. Many years more he lived facing the curve of gulf, the sparkling sea, and the smiles of earth. A decree of the gods was necessary. Mercury came and seized the impudent man by the collar and, snatching him from his joys, led him forcibly back to the underworld, where his rock was ready for him.

You have already grasped that Sisyphus is the absurd hero. He *is,* as much through his passions as through his torture. His scorn of the gods, his hatred of death, and his passion for life won him that unspeakable penalty in which the whole being is exerted toward accomplishing nothing. This is the price that must be paid for the passion of this earth.

Nothing is told us about Sisyphus in the underworld. Myths are made for the imagination to breathe life into them. As for this myth, one sees merely the whole effort of a body straining to raise the huge stone, roll it and push it up a slope a hundred times over; one sees the face screwed up, the cheek tight against the stone, the shoulder bracing the clay-covered mass, the foot wedging it, the fresh start with arms outstretched, the wholly human security of two earth-clotted hands. At the very end of his long effort measured by skyless space and time without depth, the purpose is achieved. Then Sisyphus watches the stone rush down in a few moments toward that lower world whence he will have to push it up again toward the summit. He goes back down to the plain.

It is during that return, that pause, that Sisyphus interests me. A face that toils so close to stones is already stone itself! I see that man going back down with a heavy yet measured step toward the torment of which he will never know the end. That hour like a breathing-space which returns as surely as his suffering, that is the hour of consciousness. At each of those moments when he leaves the heights and gradually sinks toward the lairs of the gods, he is superior to his fate. He is stronger than his rock.

If this myth is tragic, that is because its hero is conscious. Where would his torture be, indeed, if at every step the hope of succeeding upheld him? The workman of today works every day of his life at the same tasks, and this fate is no less absurd. But it is tragic only at the rare moments when it becomes conscious. Sisyphus, proletarian of the gods, powerless and rebellious, knows the whole extent of his wretched condition: it is what he thinks of during his descent. The lucidity that was to constitute his torture at the same time crowns his victory. There is no fate that cannot be surmounted by scorn.

If the descent is thus sometimes performed in sorrow, it can also take place in joy. This word is not too much. Again I fancy Sisyphus returning toward his rock, and the sorrow was in the beginning. When the images of earth cling too tightly to memory, when the call of happiness becomes too insistent, it happens that melancholy rises in man's heart: this is the rock's victory, this is the rock itself. The boundless grief is too heavy to bear. These are our nights of Gethsemane. But crushing truths perish from being acknowledged. Thus, Œdipus at the outset obeys fate without knowing it. But from the moment he knows, his tragedy begins. Yet at the same moment, blind and desperate, he realizes that the only bond linking him to the world is the cool hand of a girl. Then a tremendous remark rings out: "Despite so many ordeals, my advanced age and the nobility of my soul make me conclude that all is well." Sophocles' Œdipus, like Dostoevsky's Kirilov, thus gives the recipe for the absurd victory. Ancient wisdom confirms modern heroism.

One does not discover the absurd without being tempted to write a manual of happiness. "What! by such narrow ways—?" There is but one world, however. Happiness and the absurd are two sons of the same earth. They are inseparable. It would be a mistake to say that happiness necessarily springs from the absurd discovery. It happens as well that the feeling of the absurd springs from happiness. "I conclude that all is well," says Œdipus, and that remark is sacred. It echoes in the wild and limited universe of man. It teaches that all is not, has not been, exhausted. It drives out of this world a god who had come into it with dissatisfaction and a preference for futile sufferings. It makes of fate a human matter, which must be settled among men.

All Sisyphus' silent joy is contained therein. His fate belongs to him. His rock is his thing. Likewise, the absurd man, when he contemplates his torment, silences all the idols. In the universe suddenly restored to its silence, the myriad wondering little voices of the earth rise up. Unconscious, secret calls, invitations from all the faces, they are the necessary reverse and price of victory. There is no sun without shadow, and it is essential to know the night. The absurd man says yes and his effort will henceforth be unceasing. If there is a personal fate, there is no higher destiny, or at least there is but one which he concludes is inevitable and despicable.[3] For the rest, he knows himself to be the master of his days. At that subtle moment when man glances backward over his life, Sisyphus returning toward his rock, in that slight pivoting he contemplates that series of unrelated actions which becomes his fate, created by him, combined under his memory's eye and soon sealed by his death. Thus, convinced of the wholly human origin of all that is human, a blind man eager to see who knows that the night has no end, he is still on the go. The rock is still rolling.

I leave Sisyphus at the foot of the mountain! One always finds one's burden again. But Sisyphus teaches the higher fidelity that negates the gods and raises rocks. He too concludes that all is well. This universe henceforth without a master seems to him neither sterile nor futile. Each atom of that stone, each mineral flake of that night-filled mountain, in itself forms a world. The struggle itself toward the heights is enough to fill a man's heart. One must imagine Sisyphus happy.

[1] **highwaymen:** robbers who steal from travellers along public roads
[2] **levity:** lack of seriousness
[3] **despicable:** worthy of being despised or hated

A CLOSER LOOK

1. What was the eternal punishment to which Sisyphus was condemned? What were the several possible causes of his eternal conditions? Do you think any of his deeds on earth justified his eternal task? Why, or why not?

2. Albert Camus says, "Myths are made for the imagination to breathe life into them." What do you think he means by this? Explain using examples from what you have read.

3. "The workman of today works every day of his life at the same tasks, and this fate is no less absurd (than that of Sisyphus)." Do you agree? Why, or why not?

Issac Asimov

WORDS FROM THE MYTHS

● Isaac Asimov tells us that the ancient myths are far more than interesting fairy tales and adventure stories. They are part of our culture, and much of our language, particularly our scientific language, is derived from them.

HUMAN BEINGS WOULDN'T BE HUMAN IF THEY didn't wonder about the world about them. Many thousands of years ago, when humankind was still primitive, people must have looked out of caves and wondered about what they saw. What made the lightning flash? Where did the wind come from? Why would winter start soon and why would all the green things die? And then why did they come back to life the next spring?

People sometimes wondered about themselves, too. Why did they get sick sometimes? Why did they all get old and die eventually? Who first taught humans how to use fire and how to weave cloth?

There were any number of questions but there were no answers. These were the days before science; before people had learned to experiment in order to determine the hows and whys of the universe.

What early peoples had to do was to invent what seemed to be the most logical answers. The raging wind was like the blowing of an angry man. The wind, however, was much stronger than the breath of any ordinary man and it had been blowing ever since anyone could remember. Therefore, the wind must be created by a tremendously huge and powerful man, one who never died. Such a superhuman being was a "god" or "demon."

The lightning seemed, perhaps, the huge, deadly spear of another god. Then, since arrows killed men, disease could be the result of invisible arrows fired by still another god.

Since men and women married and had children, perhaps the green plants of the world were the children of the sky (a god) and the earth (a goddess). The gentle rain which made the plants grow was the marriage between them.

Perhaps a goddess was in charge of the plants of the world and grew angry because of some misfortune. She might have refused to let the plants grow until things had been straightened out That was why the green things died and winter came and that's why the world grew green again when winter was over and spring came.

Every group of human beings made up such stories; and some groups were more interesting and clever at it than others. Foremost in excellence were the ancient Greeks. They were a lively, imaginative people with great literary talents, and they made up some of the most fascinating tales of this sort.

The Greeks took their myths very seriously. Since the gods controlled natural forces, it was wise to treat them with careful consideration. They had to be bribed to send rain when it was needed, and pleaded with not to send disease or misfortune. For that reason, animals were sacrificed to them, beautiful temples were built for them, songs were composed to praise them. Thus, a religion grew up about the myths.

After Christianity was established, the old religion died out and Europeans no longer believed in the old Greek and Roman gods. The old literature was not allowed to die; it was too great to be allowed to die. In fact, the old Greek stories were so fascinating that even after Christianity was established, people did not consider themselves really educated unless and until they had learned those stories. Educated people introduced words from the myths into their speaking and some of those words remained in the language. For that reason, traces of the Greek myths are to be found today in every European tongue, including English.

For instance, a police car's signal is a siren and a sea cow is a sirenian. A circus organ is a calliope; a jelly-fish is a medusa; and an Australian anteater is an echidna. We call out in a stentorian voice; listen to a kindly mentor or a bearded nestor; despise a hectoring bully. In every case mentioned, we are drawing upon the Greek stories where a Siren was a death trap, Calliope a goddess, Medusa and Echidna horrible monsters, and Stentor, Mentor, Nestor, and Hector were men.

Scientists, particularly, drew upon the old myths. Until quite recently, Latin and Greek were the common languages of learned men of all nations. When some new animal or planet or chemical or phenomenon needed to be named, it would have been inconvenient if scientists of each nationality used names drawn from their own language. The habit arose of giving a Latin or Greek name which all nationalities could use.

Since the Greek myths are so well known it was natural to take words from those myths whenever they seemed to fit the situation. For instance, when uranium was first being broken down by fission during World War II, a new element was found amid the deadly radioactive heat. It was named "promethium" after Prometheus, a character of the Greek myths who dared the deadly radioactive heat of the sun to bring fire to humanity.

Most of us are introduced to Greek myths in childhood but are taught to think of them only as interesting fairy tales and adventure stories. However, as you can see, they are more than that. They are part of our culture, and much of our language, particularly our scientific language, is derived from them. The Greek myths—old, old stories, which have been living now for three thousand years, still penetrate our daily lives. By understanding the myths, we will understand ourselves better.

A CLOSER LOOK

1. Why did the ancient peoples invent myths? How did these ancient stories become an early religion?

2. Why have we continued to study the myths even though the religion of the ancient Greeks is no longer followed?

3. "By understanding the myths, we will understand ourselves better." Do you agree with this statement by Isaac Asimov? Why, or why not?

John Keats

ODE ON A GRECIAN URN

I

Thou still unravished bride of quietness
    Thou foster-child of Silence and slow Time,
Sylvan[1] historian, who canst thus express
    A flowery tale more sweetly than our rhyme:
What leaf-fringed legend haunts about thy shape
    Of deities or mortals, or of both,
        In Tempë or the dales of Arcady?[2]
    What men or gods are these? What maidens loth?[3]
What mad pursuit? What struggle to escape?
        What pipes and timbrels? What wild ecstasy?

II

Heard melodies are sweet, but those unheard
    Are sweeter; therefore, ye soft pipes, play on;
Not to the sensual ear, but more endeared
    Pipe to the spirit ditties[4] of no tone:
Fair youth, beneath the trees, thou canst not leave
    Thy song, nor ever can those trees be bare;
        Bold Lover, never, never canst thou kiss,
Though winning near the goal—yet, do not grieve;
        She cannot fade, though thou hast not thy bliss,
    For ever wilt thou love, and she be fair!

III

Ah, happy, happy boughs! that cannot shed
    Your leaves, nor ever bid the Spring adieu;
And, happy melodist, unwearièd,
    For ever piping songs for ever new;
More happy love! more happy, happy love!
    For ever warm and still to be enjoyed,
        For ever panting, and for ever young;
All breathing human passion far above,
    That leaves a heart high-sorrowful and cloyed,
        A burning forehead, and a parching tongue.

IV

Who are these coming to the sacrifice?
  To what green altar, O mysterious priest,
Leadest thou that heifer lowing at the skies,
    And all her silken flanks with garlands drest?
What little town by river or sea shore,
  Or mountain-built with peaceful citadel,
    Is emptied of this folk, this pious morn?
And, little town, thy streets for evermore
  Will silent be; and not a soul to tell
    Why thou art desolate, can e'er return.

V

O Attic[5] shape! Fair attitude! with brede[6]
  Of marble men and maidens overwrought,
With forest branches and the trodden weed;
    Thou, silent form, dost tease us out of thought
As doth eternity: Cold Pastoral![7]
    When old age shall this generation waste,
    Thou shalt remain, in midst of other woe
Than ours, a friend to man, to whom thou say'st,
  "Beauty is truth, truth beauty," — that is all
    Ye know on earth, and all ye need to know.

[1] **sylvan:** woodland
[2] **Tempe and Arcady:** places in Greek mythology associated with gods and shepherds
[3] **loth:** reluctant or unwilling
[4] **ditties:** songs
[5] **Attic:** associated with Attica (where Athens was the major city)
[6] **brede:** braid (as a border)
[7] **Pastoral:** work of art representing the shepherd's life